THREE CENTURIES OF FRENCH ART

VOLUME II

Cover:
Pierre Auguste Renoir
Reclining Nude
Plate 41

THREE CENTURIES
OF FRENCH ART

Volume II

Selections from
The Norton Simon, Inc. Museum of Art
and the Norton Simon Foundation

THE FINE ARTS MUSEUMS OF SAN FRANCISCO:

CALIFORNIA PALACE OF THE LEGION OF HONOR

Exhibited at the California Palace of the Legion of Honor
beginning October 19th, 1974.

Copyright © 1975 by The Fine Arts Museums of San Francisco
ISBN 0-88401-008-2
Library of Congress Catalogue Card No. 75-37417.

Designed by Adrian Wilson in collaboration with Lanier Graham
Produced by Suzan Reed & Bob Ross
Copy edited by Ann Karlstrom
Composed by Mackenzie-Harris Corp. in Centaur and Arrighi types
Printed by Phelps-Schaefer Litho-Graphics Co.

Editorial Staff

GENERAL EDITOR:
F. Lanier Graham

EDITOR OF VOLUME II:
Jacques de Caso

BIOGRAPHICAL SKETCHES BY:
F. Lanier Graham
with the assistance of
William H. Elsner &
Rosemary Gilbert

REMARKS BY:
Lani Abbott
Robert Atkins
Judith Bernstein
Timothy Chasson
Cathy Curtis
Michael Driskel
Mary Durantini
Kevin Hubbard
Gail Joyce
Martha Hoeprich Kennedy
Rebecca Love
Lynn Pudles
Mary Ritter
Dianne Sachko
Merrill Schleier
Meredith Ann Shedd
Beth Wright

HISTORICAL LISTINGS:
Compiled by Darryl E. Isley &
edited by Marion C. Stewart, under
the supervision of William H. Elsner

GENERAL BIBLIOGRAPHY:
Compiled by Marion C. Stewart
with the assistance of
Michael Driskel &
Meredith Ann Shedd

Alphabetical List of
Catalogue & Plate Numbers

Contents

Foreword

One of the most interesting things in America's social history is how old institutions can be transformed into dynamic new ones. Six years ago when there was talk of trying to merge San Francisco's two Old Master art museums into one, most people were very doubtful that such a thing could ever take place. No one had ever heard of two major museums merging before. It has been a pleasure to watch the hoped-for synthesis actually take place under the able leadership of the new administration and an outstanding staff. It has been rewarding to encourage the excellent master-plan of The Fine Arts Museums of San Francisco in its new direction by placing on extended loan the major portion of our foundations' French collection. We are hopeful that the visitors to the Legion of Honor will be pleased with the many new additions presented in this new catalogue.

NORTON SIMON

FIGURE I, Detail from Nicolas de Largillière, Plate 3.

Preface

Just over three years will have elapsed between the arrival in San Francisco of the Norton Simon French collection in May 1973 and its departure for The Norton Simon Museum of Art at Pasadena in July 1976. An estimated 1,500,000 visitors will have seen the collection at the Legion of Honor. This munificent loan was a welcome enrichment at a time when the California Palace of the Legion of Honor, by merging with the M. H. de Young Memorial Museum, had become the only museum in America devoted to the arts of France. It filled important gaps and added many masterpieces to enjoy and study.

The Norton Simon loan is an extremely rare exception to the usual pattern of special exhibitions that can be seen for only six or eight weeks. As such, it has had many far-reaching advantages. The exhibition has not been a single, static event with works hung in a fixed arrangement, but a dynamic series of experiences which evolved in several phases. For the first year and a half the Simon paintings were seen together chronologically beside a gallery of sculpture by Maillol ranging from *Chained Action*—a female nude of gigantic scale—to the intimacy of six small figure studies. Three of Rodin's monumental bronzes—*Walking Man, The Burghers of Calais* and *Balzac*—provided the visual focus for reinstalling the Museum's own extensive Rodin collection in renovated galleries that were dedicated on the Fiftieth Anniversary of the Legion of Honor in November of 1974.

During the following year the Maillol sculpture and some of the paintings were withdrawn, but the size of the exhibition virtually doubled with the addition of almost 50 paintings. An entirely new arrangement was developed melding the old and new Simon loans with the Museum's permanent collection. Key works or whole galleries of Simon loans were placed where they best fitted in the history of French art. This sophisticated use of the loans allowed the works of art "to reverberate harmoniously with those of its neighbors," Lanier Graham observed, saying "when an entire gallery is filled with related works of art, the richness of the interaction is so great that the multiplying effect of the aesthetic experience expands geometrically."

Moreover, this integration of collections made possible a number of effective teaching comparisons. In the same gallery one could study a pair of paintings from the school of Poussin in the Museum collection and *Camillus and the Schoolmaster of Falerii,* a well-documented work by Poussin from the Simon collection. Beside a masterful still life by Cézanne one could examine an interesting copy by Redon.

In many ways, the spiritual and educative contribution of this experience to the life of our community goes far beyond what can be measured. But the response from colleges and universities can be gauged precisely. For example, a number of professors have observed that this is the first time, locally, that they have been able to teach the history of French painting comprehensively from actual examples.

The first volume of this Catalogue documented the works that went on view in the spring of 1973. This second volume documents the works that went on view in fall of 1974. The manner in which Volume II was prepared, in association with the University of California at Berkeley, is vivid testimony to the new intensity of the educational program of The Fine Arts Museums of San Francisco.

IAN McKIBBIN WHITE
Director of Museums

FIGURE II, Detail from Vincent van Gogh, Plate 46.

Introduction

The preparation of this catalogue has been a major experiment in cooperation between The Fine Arts Museums of San Francisco and the University of California at Berkeley. During the last several years we have engaged in numerous programs with Bay-Area colleges and universities. To date, this has been the most complex, and in many ways, the most rewarding of these educational experiments.

The program developed in the following way. Most of the work on Volume I (published in 1973) was done by members of the Museum staff. As Volume II approached, we realized that for the same people to do another book would not be taking full advantage of a unique opportunity.

On the one hand, there was an extraordinary collection that needed to be catalogued. On the other hand were a number of local colleges and universities with graduate programs in art history, but no courses in how to write a catalogue. Moreover, universities rarely are able to offer their students an opportunity to work at length with original works of art of outstanding quality. Most of the time is spent studying photographs and slides.

During the summer of 1973, our inquiries were warmly received. Robert Brawley and Debbie Kirshman of Lone Mountain College in San Francisco decided to offer a graduate seminar in "The Writing of an Art Catalogue"—a wide-ranging experience that was philosophical, historical and practical. Leopold Ettlinger, Chairman of the Department of Art History at U.C. Berkeley was particularly enthusiastic about the educational potential of the project. When we discussed the idea with Jacques de Caso, it was decided that a special two-quarter seminar of independent study would be devoted to "The Cataloguing of an Art Collection." Under the guidance of Professor de Caso, the first drafts for these entries were prepared by the graduate students in the Spring of 1975. During the summer that preliminary work was edited into an abbreviated form under the supervision of Professor de Caso by Michael Driskel and Meredith Shedd. During the fall, these manuscripts were prepared for publication by Bill Elsner, Marion Stewart, Rosemary Gilbert and myself.

The preparation of this catalogue has been a richly educational experience for all of us. We discovered that our collective energy, our synergy, is much greater than the sum of our separate institutional potentials. As Ian White said to Professor Ettlinger at the conclusion of our preliminary discussion, "you are the text book; we are the illustrations." By merging our resources we have been able to develop this two-volume tool for the study of French art that we hope will be useful for many years to come.

F. Lanier Graham
Chief Curator

Catalogue of the Exhibition

This catalogue is arranged in an approximate chronological order. The date of each work is given after the title. If the date is given in parentheses it is because the year does not actually appear on the work itself, but has been determined by historical references and/or stylistic analysis. Dimensions are given in inches and centimeters, height preceding width. As a rule, literary references have been limited to those which mention or discuss the individual work being catalogued. References from exhibition catalogues are cited under exhibitions.

F.L.G.

Sébastien Stoskopff

Born 1597 in Strasbourg; died 1657.

Early in his life he was apprenticed to Daniel Soreau, a Walloon painter who lived near Antwerp and died in 1619. After Soreau's death, Stoskopff continued his workshop. It was from Soreau that Stoskopff absorbed the influence of Flemish still-life painting. About 1621 he went to Paris where he lived until 1641. During this period, he reintegrated himself with the French tradition. His realism became more simple and more clearly focused. Stoskopff returned to Strasbourg in 1641. There he seems to have been very well received. It was during this last era that, with considerable confidence, he produced most of his best work.

1. STILL LIFE WITH EMPTY GLASSES (1644)
Oil on canvas, 34 x 43-1/4 in. (86.4 x 109.9 cm.)

REFERENCES

M. FARÉ, "*La Nature Morte en France*, Editions Cailler, Geneva. (To be included in the new edition.)

COLLECTIONS

Private Collection, Vienna;
Paul Rosenberg & Co., New York;
The Norton Simon Foundation, Los Angeles (1972).

REMARKS

This mysterious still life appears to represent the aftermath of a drinking bout. Glasses which have been washed in the metal basin are drying in a basket, though one has slipped from the stick with an attached brush (which was used to pluck the glasses safely from the water) and has broken into three pieces. A screw-capped metal bottle still sits in the basin. In contrast to the disorder of the fallen wicker-sheathed bottle and glass on the left, a neat stack of metal tumblers on the right is placed next to a single glass which is perhaps dangerously near the edge of the table. The arrangement of objects in space is unusual: the table in the foreground rests against part of a fireplace. Within the room on the right is another table with the basket of glasses. In a recess in the far wall is another, almost hallucinatory glass filled with liquid. As a result of his early apprenticeship with a Flemish Protestant refugee painter and his subsequent years in Paris, Stoskopff's work reveals the influence of early, loosely-composed Flemish still lifes as well as the spare, refined spirit of the painters of St. Germain-des-Pres. It is the passage of time which seems to fascinate the painter: fragile glass will break suddenly just as life will one day be taken away without warning. The thin, transparent glasses almost absorbed by the darkness create a mystical, otherworldly aura which is heightened by the visionary glass in the niche. The depiction of Strasbourg-crafted silver and glassware and the date of the artist's two versions of *A Basket of Glasses* suggest this last productive decade for this painting as well.
C.C.

Louise Moillon

Born about 1610 in Paris; died 1696.

Biographical sketch in Volume I.

2. BOWL OF CURAÇAO ORANGES. 1634

Oil on panel, 18-1/4 x 25-1/2 in.
(46.4 x 64.8 cm.)
Signed and dated, lower right: "Louyse Moillon
1634"

REFERENCES
J. WILHELM, "Louise Moillon," *L'Oeil* (September 1956),
  p. 6, no. 21, repr.
M. FARÉ, *La Nature Morte en France* (1962), I, repr. in color
  opp. p. 88.

EXHIBITIONS
Paris, Galerie Andre Weil, "Le Nature Morte et son
  Inspiration," 1960, no. 43.

COLLECTIONS
Mme. Pierre Lamy, Paris;
Herner-Wengraf, Ltd., London;
The Norton Simon Foundation, Los Angeles (1972).

REMARKS

Louise Moillon, one of the finest of the small group of
women artists in the seventeenth century, spent nearly
her entire life painting precise, quiet still lifes of fruit
(and sometimes vegetables) in baskets or bowls. Although her earliest known painting dates from 1629,
when she was nineteen years old, and the last seems to
have been executed in 1674, her style never changed.
The orderly, decorative, yet minutely true-to-life still
lifes, arranged along the length of tables that are slightly
tilted toward the viewer, follow the tradition of the
earliest Dutch and Flemish still-life painters. This
particular painting stands out from Moillon's other
works by virtue of the exotic nature of the fruit—ex-
ploited for the contrast between its oddly curled knobs
and the slight curves of the leaves—in place of the
peaches, cherries and grapes more common to the
artist's oeuvre. What makes Louise Moillon's art so
appealing is its painstaking quality, the naive gravity of
the small-sized canvases (generally signed and dated
neatly on the side of the table) combined with an ex-
traordinarily convincing depiction of the textures of
the round natural objects and their china or wicker
containers. Each work is a quietly musical poem.
C.C.

19

Nicolas de Largillière

Born 1656 in Paris; died 1746.

Biographical sketch in Volume I.

3. MARQUIS D'HAVRINCOURT

Oil on canvas, 32 x 25-1/2 in. (81.3 x 64.8 cm.)

REFERENCES

J. FITZSIMMONS, "Rococo in a New Setting," *The Art Digest* (15 November 1952), pp. 15-16.
P. McCARTHY, *The Globe and Mail*, Toronto, 24 January 1953, repr.
H. A. LA FARGE, "French Seventeenth Century," *Art News* (April 1960), p. 12.
S. TILLIM, *Arts* (April 1960), p. 56, repr.

EXHIBITIONS

New York, Duveen Brothers, Inc., "French Art in Painting and Sculpture of the Eighteenth Century," 23 October-22 November 1952, no. 6.
London (Ontario), University of Western Ontario, "17th-18th Century French Masters," February-March 1953, repr.
Palm Beach, Society of the Four Arts, "Portraits, A Record of Changing Tastes," February 1964, no. 4.
London, Royal Academy, "France in the Eighteenth Century," 6 January-3 March 1968, no. 407.

COLLECTIONS

Alphonse Pierre de Cardevac, Marquis d'Havrincourt, Château Havrincourt, Pas-de-Calais, France;
Duveen Brothers, Inc., New York;
The Norton Simon Foundation, Los Angeles (1965).

REMARKS

This dignified and opulent image of the Marquis was painted according to the formula endorsed by the prestigious French Academy, of which Largillière was a member. According to academic doctrine, history painting was the most serious and ennobling genre in art, and portraitists sought defense for their own work in incorporating some of the standard appurtenances of history painting such as the column and the crimson drapery which swirls around the Marquis's costume with a rather theatrical flourish. These artistic conventions had the effect of solemnizing portraiture. A portrait was less an observation of an individualized personality than an affirmation of a sitter's social significance. It was therefore a simple matter to formalize portraiture with devices which referred to wealth and influence: the heavy velvet coat with its gold buttons, the elaborate wig, and the neatly painted lace arranged at the neck with so much studied carelessness. All this swathing tended to obscure personal mannerisms which might otherwise particularize a sitter's appearance, but it gave the upper classes an image of intelligible regularity. In this social "communications system" the status of the sitter was often of more immediate importance than his personality.
L.A.

Jean-Baptiste Siméon Chardin

Born 1699 in Paris; died 1779.

Biographical sketch in Volume I.

4. DOG AND GAME (1730)

Oil on canvas, 75-3/4 x 54-3/4 in.
(192.5 x 139 cm.)

REFERENCES

LAZAREFF, *Chardin* (1947), repr.
G. WILDENSTEIN, *Chardin* (1921), no. 676, Fig. 69, repr.
D. WILDENSTEIN, *Chardin* (1969) no. 69, Fig. 33, repr.

COLLECTIONS

Aved Collection (sale, Paris, 24 November 1766, no. 132);
Aved Collection (sale, Paris, 1770, no. 132);
Passalagna Collection (sale, 18-19 March 1853, no. 111);
Private Russian Collection, c. 1910;
Wildenstein & Co., Inc., Paris;
Enrico de Santamarina, Buenos Aires;
A. M. Ramon J. Santamarina, Buenos Aires;
Galerie Schmit, Paris;
The Norton Simon Foundation, Los Angeles (1972).

REMARKS

Although the name Chardin usually conjures up images of warmly lit genre scenes and still-life paintings of gleaming kitchenware and food, the hunting still life held strong interest for this artist, who was one of the leading painters of still life in the eighteenth century. In the foreground of the painting a gracefully poised hunting dog stands with his head and glance directed outward to the left. Against the animate form of the dog, the artist juxtaposes the inanimate forms of a large hare and bird which are suspended, head down, from the branch of a tree. Slightly behind the dead animals hang a game bag, powder box, and hunting horn. The small forms of two young rabbits and a pheasant lie about the stock of a rifle which visually links the still life of game and hunting gear with the ground below and tree branch above. The subtle harmony and interrelationship between the carefully balanced forms of the dog, dead game, and hunting equipment also characterize other game still lifes by Chardin. The setting provides a dark backdrop which complements the subtle, subdued tones of the main subjects. Employing an extremely fine, soft brush stroke, the artist skillfully differentiates between the textures of the hare's fur and the bird's feathers.

M.K.

François Boucher

Born 1703 in Paris; died 1770.

Son of an obscure lace designer, he studied with Lemoyne (1688-1737) and was influenced by Watteau, Rubens and Northern Mannerism. He traveled with Carle Van Loo in 1727 to Italy where he was moved by Veronese, Ricci and Tiepolo. Returning to Paris in 1731, he married one of his beautiful models and had three children. He entered the Academy in 1734, and his career flourished under the patronage of Madame de Pompadour, his drawing pupil and friend, between 1746 and 1764. During the 1760's he was appointed Supervisor of the Tapestry Works at Gobelins and Beauvais as well as the Porcelain Works at Sèvres, Director of the Royal Academy, and First Painter to the King. During those halcyon days of the Rococo hardly any of the arts escaped Boucher's fervent attention. In no small part it was due to the heated intensity of his enormous creativity that distinctions between the "Fine Arts" and the "Decorative Arts" began to melt together into one robustly undulating whole.

5. VERTUMNUS AND POMONA (ca. 1740-45)
Oil on canvas, 62-3/4 x 66-3/8 in.
(159.4 x 168.6 cm.)

REFERENCES
P. DE NOLHAC, *François Boucher* (1907), p. 127.
A. MICHEL, *François Boucher* (n.d.), no. 349.
H. MACFALL, *Boucher* (1908), indexed p. 153.

COLLECTIONS
Prince Anatole Demidoff, Palais San Donato, Florence;
Prince Paul Demidoff, Palais San Donato, Florence (sale, Florence, 1880, no. 782);
Emile de Girardin, Paris (sale, Paris, 1883);
Ira Spanierman, Inc., New York;
The Norton Simon Foundation, Los Angeles (1970).

REMARKS
This painting depicts three women seated in a forest glade. In the foreground a young woman twists away from us as she gazes to the left and gestures toward the central character. Her contorted pose and open gesture suggest surprise and a protective attitude toward the central figure before her. The main figure of the group is a reclining nude whose pose is almost identical but seen frontally. Her gesture may be one of greeting as well as an attempt to shield her face. Behind her kneels an elaborately costumed old woman who leans forward to whisper something in her ear while lifting the drapery from her shoulder. Both nudes are illuminated by a strong light falling from the left. The title of this work, *Vertumnus and Pomona*, which comes from a story in Ovid (*Metamorphoses*, book XIV), may be inaccurate for several reasons. While Boucher did many versions of the myth, in none is the story interpreted in quite the manner we find here. In the others Pomona is dressed and listens to Vertumnus's tale as he visits her, dressed as an old woman, trying to win her love. The apparent reason for believing that our work illustrates a scene from this story is the presence of the old woman and the outdoor setting. This myth, however, cannot account for the striking reaction of "Pomona" here, for instead of responding to the woman, she directs her attention in the opposite direction. Nor does it explain the directed nature of the light, the presence and reaction of the foreground figure, and the forest setting rather than the usual cultivated garden. The Ovidian story which most closely fits the activities of the figures is perhaps that of *Jupiter and Semele* (*Metamorphoses*, book III). In the myth Juno, disguised as Semele's old nurse, encourages the girl to demand that her lover, Jupiter, appear to her in all his divine glory. When he complies she is consumed by his brilliance. The painter may have combined two moments in the story (not unusual in the eighteenth century)—Juno advising Semele and the arrival of Jupiter on the scene. There are several features in this work which are unusual in Boucher's art: the large scale, the monumentally proportioned figures, the broad brushstrokes with which the flesh is rendered, and the loosely treated landscape setting. The theme of voluptuous women involved in pastoral romances or disporting themselves in sylvan glades is at the essence of his example, however. The painting is a fragment, missing perhaps as much as 12 inches on the left side. The provenance has been traced to the 1880 sale of the San Donato collection. The attribution is supported by a drawing ascribed to Boucher which is closely related to the main figure here.
M.D.

Claude-Joseph Vernet

Born 1714 in Avignon; died 1789.

Son of a decorator of carriages and sedan chairs who had twenty-two children, Vernet began his artistic studies under his father. At the age of twenty he left by sea for Italy where he was to study for nearly twenty years with particular interest in landscape painting. During his voyage to Italy, his ship encountered a violent storm. That experience was to have a lasting effect on Vernet's artistic career; the sea and the vessels which crossed it became his favorite subjects. Returning to France in 1753, he settled in Marseilles. In the next year he was commissioned by the Marquis of Marigny (brother of Mme. de Pompadour) to paint the twenty-four principal ports of France, a task he left only half finished. Vernet was one of the first French artists to revive the art of land- and seascape painting which had flourished in the seventeenth century.

6. THE BAY OF POSILIPO. 1762

Oil on canvas, 28-1/2 x 38 in. (72.4 x 96.5 cm.)
Signed and dated, lower right:
"Joseph Vernet 1762"

EXHIBITIONS
Poughkeepsie, New York, Vassar College Art Gallery, "Nature and Natural Phenomena in Art of the Eighteenth Century," 20 February-13 March 1964, no. 19.

COLLECTIONS
Mrs. Hannah Entwisle, England (1908);
Mrs. Loyd Harcastle, Hawkhurst, Kent, England;
Duveen Brothers, Inc., New York;
The Norton Simon Foundation, Los Angeles (1965).

REMARKS
This painting is characteristic of the art of Vernet, the most famous marine painter of the eighteenth century. In the manner of a stage-setting, the scene is framed by a beach in the foreground and by a rock to the right covered with trees. In the background one can detect the geometrical forms of the houses in the city and a long pier with a lighthouse, clearly visible through the fog. In the middle are small boats and a larger ship at anchor. Throughout the painting we see people, engagingly rendered with great attention to details of costume, attitude, and gesture, actively involved in the business of unloading the cargo and disembarking from the ship. Long shadows cast by the lightly-clad figures and the heavy mist suggest that it is still early in the morning on a spring or summer day. The site, Posilipo, is actually a hill situated along the length of the Bay of Naples. Along this hill was an old road that terminated in a cave called the "grotto of Pozzuoli," which might be the same cave that we see in the rock at the right side of the painting. Near this cave was an old tomb, reputed to be that of Virgil. In creating this harbor scene, Vernet may have wanted to temper the depiction of Posilipo as a bustling, modern port city by an allusion to the legendary and picturesque charm of the site as a memorial to one of the most admired authors of classical antiquity. Because of the great finesse with which he handled the details and the great delicacy with which he depicted the subtle nuances of light and atmosphere, this painting could be considered one of Vernet's finest works.
M.S.

Henri-Horace Roland de la Porte

Born about 1724 in Paris; died 1793.

He was a pupil of Chardin, who was the greatest still-life painter of eighteenth-century Europe. There is no way a younger artist, interested in the same subject, could escape the powerful influence of such a great master. Monsieur de la Porte began his career by imitating Chardin; indeed he was known as Chardin's "Doppelgänger" or alter-ego. He was admitted to the Royal Academy in 1763 and gradually achieved a style with its own distinctive elegance.

7. STILL LIFE (ca. 1765)
   Oil on canvas, 20-7/8 x 25-1/2 in. (53 x 64.8 cm.)

REFERENCES
D. DIDEROT, *Salons* (1960), II, pp. 142-143, no. 104.
M. FARÉ, *La Nature Morte en France* (1962), I, p. 167; II, no. 375, repr.

EXHIBITIONS
Paris, "Salon of 1765," no. 104.
Paris, Galerie Charpentier, "Natures Mortes Françaises," 1952, no. 200 (attributed to Vallayer-Coster).
Paris, Galerie Heim, "Hommage à Chardin," 6 June-10 July 1959, no. 67.
Princeton, New Jersey, The Art Museum, Princeton University, "Selections from the Norton Simon, Inc., Museum of Art," December 1972-June 1974, no. 13, repr.

COLLECTIONS
Henri Leroux, Versailles (sale, Palais Galliera, Paris, 23 March 1968, no. 86);
Old Masters Galleries, London;
The Norton Simon Inc. Foundation, Los Angeles (1968).

REMARKS
Roland de la Porte was considered by many of his contemporaries to be a master of the extreme effect of illusion known as *trompe-l'oeil*. Critics were moved to praise his work in extravagant terms: "When one knows that this is an illusion, one's eyes still refuse to believe it." It is difficult, indeed, not to appreciate the skill the artist displays in this still life. Throughout the painting he deftly presents the contrast of diverse textures: the smooth hardness of the cup, the fuzzy softness of the peaches, the waxy surface of the grapes, the granular bits of sugar, the dull metallic lustre of the tin box. Each object is modeled clearly and separately in the light that falls from the left. Nevertheless, certain devices help to unify the composition. The colors of the orange and blue patterned bowl are echoed in those of the fruit and flowers; the asymmetrical tilt of the spoon in the cup, the sprig of flowers and the half-opened lid of the tin box modify the static quality of a row of objects on a table (which also has an asymmetrical bulge on the right). And yet, the gravity and stillness of this painting is maintained by the airless quality of the undifferentiated background and shallow space and by the pure white hardness of the cup at the center of the table. This is a celebration of the concrete quality of things which are fastidiously arranged to please the eye and to tantalize the sense of touch.
C.C.

Hubert Robert

Born 1733 in Paris; died 1808.

The delicate perception of young Robert assimilated the influence of many artists, especially his close friend, Fragonard. He went to Rome in 1754 and studied at the French Academy. That landscape and the work of Piranesi and Pannini stimulated him to concentrate on open vistas filled with real or imaginary ruins. In 1765 he returned to Paris and was quite popular. The very next year be became a member of the Royal Academy, due to the sponsorship of its director, François Boucher. In 1770 he was commissioned to re-design the gardens of Versailles including the famous "Hameau" near the Petit Trianon. As a reward for his brilliant work, he was appointed Keeper of the King's Pictures in 1788. As curator of the Louvre, he designed the "master plan" for the installation of those collections which was used until the 1960's.

8. THE FOUNTAIN (ca. 1775)

Oil on canvas, 26 x 20 in. (66 x 50.8 cm.)

REFERENCES
P. DE NOLHAC, *Hubert Robert* (1910), p. 103.

EXHIBITIONS
Poughkeepsie, New York, Vassar College Art Gallery, "Hubert Robert—Paintings and Drawings," October-November 1962, no. 10.

COLLECTIONS
Presumably Trouart Collection, Paris (sale, Vente Trouart, Paris, 1779, no. 72);
Duveen Brothers, Inc., New York;
The Norton Simon Foundation, Los Angeles (1965).

REMARKS
This work unites the effects of light and a virtuoso display of brushwork in rendering the charming transience of nature. And yet, once we have been invited, through the outstretched arm of the man in the foreground, to explore the scene at our leisure, we find that there are subdued poignant references to the isolation of man and his exclusion from nature's joyful abundance. The figures at the balustrade are irretrievably separated from the play of water which they admire; the solemn lion which perhaps once graced an ancient family's estate is merely a plaything for the irreverent children of the present; the man and woman in the foreground ignore the beauties around them which their child attempts to call to their attention. The mood of the painting, an amalgam of exuberance and reverie, is echoed in the cool and silvery hues. The lavish but transitory effects of nature are opposed to the weighty relics of another age, and contemporary man must find a way to incorporate both these realms into his life. This resonating combination of historic architecture and sculpture, contemporary figures and landscape became the hallmark of Robert's style.
B.W.

Antoine Vestier

Born 1740 near Avallon; died 1824.

A pupil of the academician Jean-Baptiste Pierre, he married the daughter of the master enamelist Révérend. He traveled, studied and worked extensively in England and Holland from 1776 until he settled in Paris in 1784. As a portrait painter and miniaturist, he worked in both oil and enamel. His work was exhibited regularly in the *Salons* from 1782 to 1806; he had become a member of the academy in 1787. Although he painted a number of portraits of men, including several of officers of the musical corps of the National Guard, his subjects usually were women and children.

9. PORTRAIT OF A LADY. 1783

Oil on canvas, 30-1/8 x 26 in. (76.5 x 66 cm.)
Signed and dated, lower left: "(V)estier fecit 1783"

EXHIBITIONS

Portland, Portland Art Museum, "Recent Acquisitions by the Norton Simon, Inc. Museum of Art," November 1968-March 1969.

Princeton, New Jersey, The Art Museum, Princeton University, "Selections from the Norton Simon, Inc., Museum of Art," 2 December 1972-June 1974, no. 14, repr.

COLLECTIONS

Mrs. Bothwick Norton;
Olaf Kier;
Arthur Tooth & Sons, Ltd., London;
The Norton Simon Inc. Foundation, Los Angeles (1968).

REMARKS

During the eighteenth century, portraiture became more direct and informal as non-aristocratic families found themselves able to commission their portraits. The most intimate portraits were perhaps miniatures which were worn on the body in the form of jewelry, used as ornament for household articles, or tucked into frames and propped up on boudoir tables as personal keepsakes. Many miniaturists also painted full-scale portraits, blowing up the preciousness of their work into almost life-sized images. Antoine Vestier was among them. In this portrait he has painted the sitter with an exquisite economy of expression, design, and color which are the refinements of good miniature painting. His sitter is quietly arranged in a self-contained, motionless pose. She sits on her chair, facing her painter—calm, composed and complacent. She is flattered by the elegant simplicity of Vestier's blue and grey color scheme which echoes her grey hair. The pearl tones of her hair also reverberate in the pale tones of luxurious textiles; the blue of her eyes is supported by the blue of her gown. For all his flattery however, Vestier did not idealize his sitter as many French portraitists of the period would have done; instead he showed a predilection for direct observation which gives this portrait a distinctly personal presence.
L.A.

33

Marie-Louise-Elisabeth Vigée-Lebrun

Born 1755 in Paris; died 1842.

Daughter of Louis Vigée, a pastel portrait artist, she began her artistic career at an early age as a pupil of her father. She also studied with Greuze and Vernet and specialized in portraits of women and children. In 1774 she was admitted to the Academy of St. Luke and in 1783 to the Royal Academy. A woman of considerable charm, firmly established in her career as an artist, she was called to Versailles in 1779 to paint Marie-Antoinette. She not only painted many portraits of the Queen and her children during the next decade but also became the Queen's close personal friend. At the beginning of the revolution in 1789, she left France for many years of travel that took her to Italy, Austria and Russia, where she was received with great enthusiasm as an artist and given the sobriquet of "Mademoiselle Rubens." Except for brief periods, she did not again reside in Paris until 1810, having retired from her prolific artistic career.

10. THERESA, COUNTESS KINSKY. 1793

Oil on canvas, 53 x 39 in. (134.6 x 99 cm.)
Signed, inscribed, and dated on tree trunk, left:
"E. L. Vigée Lebrun, à Vienne, 1793"

REFERENCES

E. Vigée-Lebrun, *Souvenirs de Madame Vigée-Lebrun* (1869),
  I, pp. 269-271, 283; II, p. 368.
P. de Nolhac, *Madame Vigée-Lebrun, Peintre de la Reine
  Marie Antoinette* (1908), p. 107; repr. facing p. 106.
A. Blum, *Madame Vigée-Lebrun, Peintre des Grandes Dames du
  XVIIIe Siècle* (1914), pp. 63, 101.
W. H. Helm, *Vigée-Lebrun* (1915), pp. 118, 120, 202.
D. W. Steadman, "The Norton Simon Exhibition at
  Princeton," *Art Journal* (Fall 1972), pp. 34-40; repr. p. 36,
  Fig. 6.

EXHIBITIONS

Princeton, New Jersey, The Art Museum, Princeton
  University, "Selections from the Norton Simon, Inc.,
  Museum of Art," 2 December 1972-June 1974, no. 15,
  repr.

COLLECTIONS

Theresa, Countess Kinsky (née Princesse de Dietrichstein),
  Vienna;
Counts Clam-Gallas, Vienna;
Count Franz Clam-Gallas, Vienna;
Eleonore, Countess Radslav Kinsky, Prague;
Dr. A. de Celerin, Prague;
Schaeffer Galleries, Inc., New York;
The Norton Simon Inc. Foundation, Los Angeles (1969).

REMARKS

This dashing portrait of the unfortunate Countess Kinsky was painted during Vigée-Lebrun's self-imposed exile from revolutionary Paris. The Countess's poignant life story was one of the entertainments of the Polish court, yet when she sat for Vigée-Lebrun she impressed her painter with the independence, spirit and courage with which she endured an impossible social situation. She had been forced into an arranged marriage with a man she never met until her wedding day. Immediately after the nuptial mass, the Count Kinsky announced to his bride that he had submitted to the marriage only for their families' sake and that he was leaving her to return to the woman he loved. The Countess never saw him again. She was left in a compromising social position, neither daughter, wife, nor widow. Vigée-Lebrun, who collected extraordinary honors during her career, was widely admired by other portrait painters for her superb sense of color, her handling of flesh tones, the delicacy of her brushwork and the intelligence of her compositions. This particular portrait is one of the finer examples of her work during the decade. It reflects the international trends in Neo-classicism which she incorporated into her work after leaving Paris. Changing fashions in art and dress confounded her natural inclination for the lighter, softer palette of earlier decades. However, she was versatile. Her handling of the deep tones of the gown, the gold and coral accents and the abstract remoteness of the composition make this a brilliant painting.
L.A.

Claude Michel (called Clodion)

Born 1738 in Nancy; died 1814.

Son of two sculptors and student of Jean-Baptiste Pigalle, he was the leading sculptor of the time. He won the *Prix de Rome* in 1762 and worked in Italy for ten years. Catherine the Great tried to attract him to Russia, but he preferred to return to Paris in 1771 and marry the daughter of Pajou. Inspired by the nymphs and satyrs of antiquity, he brought the spontaneous, hedonistic spirit of the Rococo style to its ultimate sculptural refinement.

11. A BACCHANTE SUPPORTED BY
    BACCHUS AND A FAUN 1795
    Terra cotta, H: 20 in. (50.8 cm.)
    Signed and dated: "Clodion 1795"

REFERENCES
Anon., *Le Cabinet de l'Amateur et de l'Antiquaire* (1842), I,
    pp. 45, 47, and 94.
J. VACQUIER, *Les Vieux Hôtels de Paris* (1913), I, p. 4; II (1919),
    p. 1.

COLLECTIONS
Alphonse Adel Alfred Regnier, Comte de Groneau, Marquis
    de Massa;
Caroline-Adelaide-Andreine Leroux;
André-Helene, Baron Roger;
Duveen Brothers, Inc., New York;
The Norton Simon Foundation, Los Angeles (1965).

REMARKS
In this graceful sculpture of a Bacchanalian group, Clodion works in terra cotta, a medium he frequently used for his many representations of classical subjects. Here a Bacchante is carried by the god Bacchus on the right, while a faun supports the Bacchante to her left. In addition, Bacchus carries on his left shoulder a small Cupid. At the bottom of the sculpture is an overturned wine vessel with wine and grapes spewing from it. The relationships between the figures and elements of the sculpture are complex and closely interwoven, so that the impression is one of unity rather than a group of several parts. The Bacchante unites the figures with her left arm extended to rest on the faun's shoulder, while with her right arm she embraces Bacchus and the Cupid. Another interrelationship is carried out by the garland which Bacchus holds so that it flows diagonally across his chest, and then weaves through the rest of the composition. The wine vessel at the bottom emphasizes the horizontal support upon which the Bacchante is carried, and at the same time it is captured as an integral part of the composition by Bacchus as he steps over it into the next moment.
W.H.E.

Louis-Léopold Boilly

Born 1761 in La Basée, near Lille; died 1845.

Son of the sculptor J. P. Boilly, who gave him most of his training. Early in his career he worked locally as a portraitist. In 1785 he arrived in Paris, where he continued to blend the influences of Fragonard, Greuze and Vigée-Lebrun, and such Dutch masters as Pieter de Hooch, together with careful observations from real life. His charming, anecdotal pictures became very popular as engravings. On returning from America in 1788, he painted portraits of Lafayette, Robespierre, and many other revolutionaries. Soon after his first *Salon* of 1791, he earned the respect of all the New Regime by his *Triumph of Marat* (Museum of Fine Arts, Lille). During his unusually energetic career, he produced more than 500 genre paintings and approximately 5,000 small portraits, together with numerous drawings and lithographs (at that time a recently invented medium). Both as a genre painter and portraitist, Boilly was the most talented and accurate "reporter" of the daily life of upper-middle-class France between the reign of Louis XVI and the Revolution of 1848.

12. THE INTERRUPTED SUPPER (pair)

Oil on canvas, 15 x 18 in. each (38.1 x 45.7 cm.)

REFERENCES

H. HARRISSE, *Louis Léopold Boilly: peintre, dessinateur, et lithographe* (1898), pp. 124, 135, nos. 448 (as "Poussez Ferme") and 554 (as "Le Veillard Jalous").

EXHIBITIONS

Paris, Musée Carnavalet, "Exposition L. L. Boilly," 1930, nos. 28, 29.
Princeton, New Jersey, The Art Museum, Princeton University, "Selections from the Norton Simon, Inc. Museum of Art," 2 December 1972-June 1974, no. 15, repr.

COLLECTIONS

Sir Richard Wallace, London;
Mme Lowenstein;
Mrs. M. T. Warde, London (sale, Christie's, London, 19 March 1965, no. 70);
Arthur Tooth and Sons, Ltd., London;
Norton Simon Inc Foundation, Los Angeles (1966).

REMARKS

When we think of French art around 1800 we tend to remember large paintings with grandiose subjects. But there were other strong artistic currents. One of them was the depiction of mildly erotic scenes of domestic, bourgeois life such as we see in these works by Boilly, the best-known painter of this type. A sequence of events is clearly implied, largely through gesture and facial expression, in the manner of a contemporary drawing-room comedy. In the first painting, a young lady is enjoying a meal in the intimate company of her lover when an older man attempts to interrupt their repast. He is held back by a second woman who holds the door shut while the lover retreats. In the other painting, the older man has finally succeeded in entering the room, where he is mocked by the two women while the lover snickers behind a screen. The confusion of the sequence of events is accentuated by the toppled furniture, untidy table, barking dog, and the lady's provocatively disheveled dress. Such *décolletage* was considered fashionable at that period. An exaggerated prettiness about the faces and figures of the youthful characters contrasts with the extreme ugliness of the old man, which verges on caricature. The two paintings together read like a cartoon. Although our pair of paintings is jointly titled, both of them were engraved under separate titles: "Push Hard" and "The Jealous Old Man." Many of Boilly's paintings are reproduced as popular engravings accompanied by captions. In certain respects, such scenes are remarkably similar to those we often see on television and in the movies today. M.S.

Jean-Baptiste Camille Corot

Born 1796 in Paris; died 1875.

Biographical sketch in Volume I.

13. VIEW OF VENICE: THE PIAZZETTA
SEEN FROM THE QUAI DES
ESCLAVONS (1834)
Oil on canvas, 18-1/2 x 27 in. (47 x 68.6 cm.)
Signed, lower left: "C. Corot"

REFERENCES

A. ROBAUT, *L'Oeuvre de Corot* (1905), II, No. 323, repr.
BERNHEIM JEUNE & CIE, *Quatre-Vingts Ans de Peinture Libre*
   (1920), repr.

EXHIBITIONS

Amsterdam, "Cent Ans de Peinture Française," April-May
   1928.
New York, M. Knoedler & Co., "A Century of French
   Painting," 12 November-8 December, 1928, no. 2, repr.
Paris, Paul Rosenberg & Co., "Le Grand Siècle," 1936.

COLLECTIONS

Van Wessen;
Arnold & Tripp, Paris (1898);
Private Collection, Paris;
Michaux, Paris;
Paul Rosenberg & Co., New York;
The Norton Simon Foundation, Los Angeles (1973).

REMARKS

Corot's painting captures the highly-lit, stage-set quality of Venice. His point of view along the Grand Canal, facing the church of Santa Maria della Salute and the Marciana Library with the Ducal palace on the right, emphasizes the architectonic relationship of the buildings on the *piazzetta*. The rhythmic repetition of their arches is played against the flat expanses of *fondamento* upon which the city stands and the sky, creating a stark, almost theatrical effect typical of the Venetian scenery. Corot's palette also captures the dreamlike harmonies of the Venetian environment. He skillfully blends the pink and beige tones of the buildings with varying hues of blue in the sky and sea by softening his color tones with the addition of white. Unlike eighteenth-century artists, Corot did not respond to the grandiose vistas of the Grand Canal. Instead, he chose more clearly defined views of specific locales in order to maximize the intense linearity of the city. He was particularly fascinated by the glistening white dome of Santa Maria della Salute and represented it in a number of canvases from different viewpoints. In reality, this church is situated closer to the embankment and therefore looms larger in relationship to the Marciana Library and Ducal palace; it appears smaller in this painting so it does not distract our attention from the exotic details in the left foreground. Corot's delicately controlled modeling of form through color influenced a number of artists, including the young Renoir whose *Le Pont des Arts*, painted a generation later, reflects Corot's skill at defining architectonic elements with color. Corot's influence extends to the mature Renoir and his fellow Impressionists who used Corot's lightened palette as a springboard for their free use of color.
D.S.

Jacques Jean Marie Achille Devéria

Born 1800 in Paris; died 1857.

A pupil of Lafitte and Girodet, he developed in the tradition of Neo-Classicism, especially under the influence of Girodet who had been a favorite pupil of David. Devéria produced a very large body of work, much of it commercial. As a painter he is best known for a large body of portraits of his contemporaries, including Victor Hugo, Alexander Dumas and Franz Liszt. Devéria was also a designer, lithographer and illustrator. In addition, he was for many years the librarian and then the curator of the *Cabinet des Estampes*. In that capacity, he contributed a great deal to the systematic classification of that famous print collection.

14. ODALISQUE

Oil on panel, 9 x 12-1/2 in. (22.8 x 31.8 cm.)
Signed, lower left: "A. Deveria"

EXHIBITIONS
Princeton, New Jersey, The Art Museum, Princeton University, "Selections from the Norton Simon,Inc., Museum of Art," 2 December 1972-June 1974, no. 19, repr.

COLLECTIONS
Private collection (sale Parke Bernet, New York, 2 March 1967, no. 95);
Norton Simon Inc Foundation, Los Angeles (1967).

REMARKS
The depiction of a languid young woman lying parallel to the picture surface and displaying her charms is part of a long tradition. In the nineteenth century, however, the treatment became more candidly erotic as the misty veil of classical allusions gradually evaporated. Here we are invited to peer into the chamber of a nubile concubine with alabaster skin. We partake of the mood of tranquil reverie, listen to the murmuring fountain, smell the acrid smoke of tobacco or hemp which she expels through parted lips, and touch the sensuous fabrics which surround her. The composition of the scene is severely geometrical, a series of carefully placed and emphasized horizontal and vertical lines. The rectilinear compositional grid and the strategically placed architectural backdrop serve to emphasize by contrast the sensuous curves of the odalisque and the sweeping silhouette of her body from the shoulder to the exquisitely delineated left foot. The most emphatic curvilinear form is the oval shape made by the relaxed hips of the young woman. The shape of the garment covering her lower body echoes the oval shape of the painting; the central point of both her garment and the canvas coincide. This center of interest is emphasized by the warm vermilion of the garment, which contrasts with the cooler, more subdued colors throughout the rest of the picture. The painting (which Devéria may have done around 1831 in conjunction with a series of lithographs of women in exotic dress) may have another dimension as well. There is reason to believe that an allegorical depiction of the five senses is alluded to here. This seems to be the intention of harem scenes by numerous earlier artists, including Ingres whom Devéria would have known.
M.D.

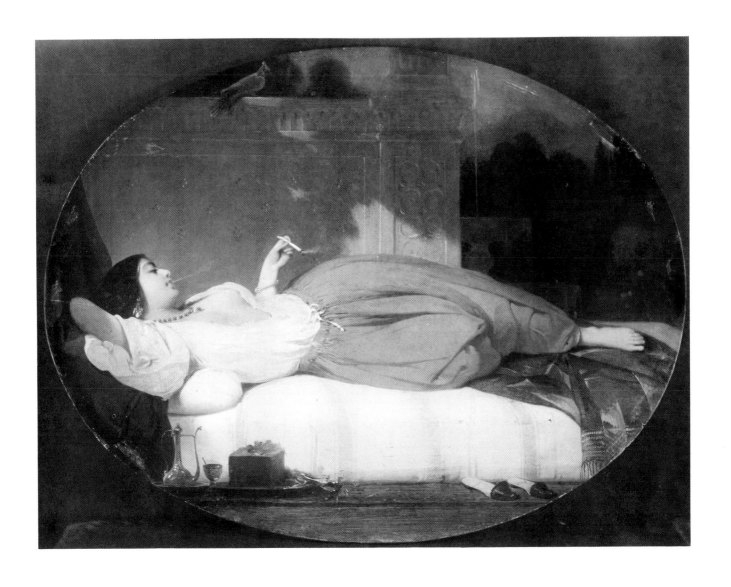

Charles François Daubigny

Born 1817 in Paris; died 1878.

Biographical sketch in Volume I.

15. HAMLET ON THE SEINE NEAR
   VERNON. 1872
   Oil on canvas, 33-1/2 x 57-1/2 in. (85.1 x
   146.1 cm.)
   Signed and dated, lower left: "Daubigny 1872"

REFERENCES

L. M. BRYANT, *What Pictures to See in America* (1915), repr.
D. W. STEADMAN, "The Landscape in Art," *University: A
   Princeton Quarterly* (Summer 1973), p. 9, repr.

EXHIBITIONS

Irvine, University of California, "A Selection of Nineteenth
   and Twentieth Century Works from the Hunt Foods &
   Industries Museum of Art Collection," March 1967, repr.
   in color, p. 8; Davis, University of California, April 1967;
   Riverside, University of California, May 1967; San Diego,
   Fine Arts Gallery, July-September 1967.
Princeton, New Jersey, The Art Museum, Princeton
   University, "Selections from the Norton Simon, Inc.
   Museum of Art," 2 December 1972-June 1974, no. 20, repr.

COLLECTIONS

M. Knoedler & Co., New York;
Corcoran Gallery of Art, Washington, D.C. (1899);
E. V. Thaw and Co., Inc., New York;
Norton Simon Inc Foundation, Los Angeles (1966).

REMARKS

Daubigny portrays the close of a day in a small village
along the lower reaches of the Seine in a landscape that
spreads a low panoramic carpet of greens beneath an
equally sweeping shell-pink sky, a composition in the
Dutch manner. Engulfed in a repetition of numerous
greens, peasants complete the day's chores. The hamlet
cottages cluster around the parish church spire—a re-
serve of warm browns and umbers on the fresh-plowed
hill overlooking the wash of green. With heavily
charged brushstrokes that set up the vibrating patterns
of lush vegetation, Daubigny creates a marshy lowland
atmosphere. The flow and movement of his brush is
recorded in the quick jabs, zig-zags, and running
waves of line in the foreground. The brushstroke, characteristic of his mature works, has a quick fluidity and
gives the briefest definition to form—qualities that
were valued by the rising generation of Impressionists
in the early 1870's and which were an important stim-
ulus for their work. In this view of a hamlet northwest
of Paris, Daubigny is dealing with his life-long favored
theme of the quiet reaches of the Seine and Oise rivers,
captured from the deck of his floating studio-boat under
the open sky. Daubigny's landscapes were very popular
with the public of his time, in spite of academic criti-
cism for their "unfinished" quality of brushwork. He
was an active and important member of the Barbizon
school of French landscapists who raised the status of
the landscape genre in painting.
G.J.

Gustave Courbet

Born 1819 in Ornans; died 1877.

Biographical sketch in Volume I.

16. THE FOREST POOL. 1865

Oil on canvas, 30 x 36 in. (76.2 x 91 cm.)
Signed and dated, lower right: "G. Courbet 65"

REFERENCES

E. NEWTON, "French Painters, VII-Courbet," *Apollo*
(November 1952), pp. 139-142, repr. p. 40, Fig. 3 (as
"Wooded Landscape").

D. W. STEADMAN, "The Landscape in Art," *University: A
Princeton Quarterly* (Summer 1973), repr. p. 9.

EXHIBITIONS

London, Lefevre Gallery, "XIX Century French Masters,"
July 1960, no. 4.

Irvine, University of California, "A Selection of Nineteenth
and Twentieth Century Works from the Hunt Foods &
Industries Museum of Art Collection," March 1967, repr.
in color, p. 7; Davis, University of California, April 1967;
Riverside, University of California, May 1967; San Diego,
Fine Arts Gallery, July-September 1967.

Princeton, New Jersey, The Art Museum, Princeton
University, "Selections from the Norton Simon, Inc.
Museum of Art," 2 December 1972-June 1974, no. 21, repr.

COLLECTIONS

Estate of the artist;
K. E. Maison, Ltd., London;
Alex Reid and Lefevre Gallery, London (1949);
Paul Kantor Gallery, Beverly Hills;
Norton Simon Inc Foundation, Los Angeles (1967).

REMARKS

The stream of *le puits noir*, or the Black Well, near Courbet's birthplace, the provincial town of Ornans, was a place he returned to throughout his life to seek respite and to paint. Our viewpoint is in the bed of the stream at the edge of a tranquil pool. The scene is closed on the right and our gaze is directed inward by a prominent mass of rock. Behind the pool the branches of the trees cover the stream, creating an inviting grotto-like bower. The wild and craggy nature of the spot is emphasized by the artist's highly innovative technique of applying paint, something which amazed contemporaries who watched him work. There is little evidence of the use of a brush in this work. To capture the quality of rock and the patterns of the water he wielded a wide palette knife to apply his paint and move it around. He used a coarse-grade canvas and dipped rags in paint which he then pressed to the surface to create seemingly spontaneous and natural textural variations. His realistic effect, however, is achieved not by attempting a meticulous reproduction of nature but by imposing his own formula on the scene. The area on the right is his personal pictorial sign for "rock," a schema he used for all manner of rocks. This master of the palette knife had a great appetite for the material and sensuous, and a deep-grained distrust for the abstract and theoretical. Unlike certain of his contemporaries who were concerned with recording fugitive light effects, he desired to recapture the permanent and essential character of things. There are no figures in the scene and there is no story. Water, rock, greenery, and their natural interaction become the subject of the work.
M.D.

Johan Barthold Jongkind

Born 1819 in Latrap, The Netherlands; died 1891.

Although Dutch by birth, Jongkind played an important role in the development of French Impressionism. Along with Boudin, he exerted strong influence on the careers of the young Monet, Stanislas Lépine, and others. He met both Boudin and Monet in 1862 and exhibited in the *Salon des Refusés* in 1863. Unlike Boudin, he did not paint in oil directly from nature but from sketches and drawings which had been done in the open air. Nevertheless he was very interested in "atmosphere." By 1864 he had begun to paint the same scenes under varying conditions of light and climate, an exercise subsequently practiced by Monet and many of the Impressionists. Unappreciated, Jongkind spent his last years in poverty and squalor.

17. VIEW OF HARFLEUR. 1852

   Oil on canvas, 17 x 23-1/4 in. (43.2 x 59.1 cm.)
   Signed and dated, lower right: "Jongkind 1852"

COLLECTIONS

Beugniet and Bonjean, Paris;
Boussod-Valadon, Paris;
Galerie Georges Petit, Paris;
Galerie Schmit, Paris;
The Norton Simon Foundation, Los Angeles (1969).

REMARKS

Harfleur, the somnolent, picturesque village we see here, was once a rich and important seaport in Normandy and the site of several momentous historical events. The church of Saint-Martin (slightly off-center in the composition) with its great flamboyant Gothic tower is a reminder of this faded glory. Our viewpoint is on the banks of the Lézarde at low tide looking toward the town. On the right we see a fishing boat with several tall masts which echo the spire of the distant church. The seamen are quietly at work repairing their gear. To the left in a prominent place we find an anecdotal scene, a mother and her small child, which is unusual in Jongkind's work. Comparing the work with photographs of the site, it is possible to see that Jongkind has observed the scene with scrupulous accuracy in many small details, yet he felt free to make adjustments to improve the visual effect. In reality the house on the extreme left is much closer to the river. The artist has moved it back and turned it so that we see more of its ornamented facade. The large chimneys to the left of the church actually exist, but the visual rhyme between the smoke they exude and the forms of the clouds behind seems hardly observed. Jongkind's vision was not that of an architect. He relied more on capturing the visual sensation than on the precise delineation of structure. The patch of orange on the house in the extreme right is an example; it is rendered as one area of color—with little concern for the fact that it covers the sharp juncture of two walls of the building. This is an early work in Jongkind's long career and a significant contribution to the new tradition of landscape painting which evoked lyrical, vignette-like qualities out of the briefly observed moment. The equilibrium he brought into this picture is something he never achieved in his own troubled life. The three most prominent motifs of the picture may imply a nostalgic desire for a stable system of values: the church as the house of God, the mother evoking the benign institution of maternity, and the seamen partaking of the saving grace of work.
M.D.

18. THE CHURCH OF ST. MEDARD. 1871

Oil on canvas, 17 x 22-1/4 in. (43.2 x 56.5 cm.)
Signed, dated, and inscribed, lower right:
"Jongkind 1871, Paris"

REFERENCES

P. NATHAN, *Dr. Fritz Nathan und Dr. Peter Nathan, 1922-1972* (1972), no. 58, repr.

EXHIBITIONS

London, Arthur Tooth and Sons, Ltd., "Anthology—Loan Exhibition of French Pictures," 1949, no. 16.
Princeton, New Jersey, The Art Museum, Princeton University, "Selections from the Norton Simon, Inc. Museum of Art," 2 December 1972-June 1974, no. 34, repr.

COLLECTIONS

Saint-Sabin, Paris;
Private Collection, England;
Arthur Tooth and Sons, Ltd., London;
Drs. Fritz and Peter Nathan, Zurich;
Norton Simon Inc Foundation, Los Angeles (1968).

REMARKS

Despite the fresh, spontaneous appearance of this picture, it was painted in the artist's Paris studio three years after an initial watercolor study. Jongkind, unlike the Impressionists who revered him, never painted directly from nature in oils. Instead, he made quick but masterful watercolor studies in which he recorded the fugitive light effects and changing atmospheric conditions of the landscape before him—often writing in color notations to assist his memory. We are situated in the rue Daubenton in Paris and look toward the apse of Saint Médard, a parish church in a quiet neighborhood on the Left Bank. It is a frosty spring morning with a sky which threatens thundershowers—a likelihood anticipated by the black cloaked figure in the foreground who carries an umbrella. There are no anecdotes and no significant actions. The drama in the scene is provided by the striking contrast of the spikey gothic tower of the old church and the opening in the dark sky through which sunlight attempts to break. The subdued color scheme with its dominant blond tonality is broken by several small but important details, such as the man with the bright red trousers, which add variety to the scene. The foreground is painted in a way reminiscent of the artist's watercolor technique, with a thin wash of oil paint over which soft, discrete brushstrokes have been added to render the texture of the unpaved street. Jongkind, knowing this neighborhood was soon to undergo a renewal project, was attempting to preserve its image on his canvas. Yet the picture is not a mere topographical record of the area; he felt free to change details to create a stronger visual impact when necessary. There is little effort at architectural exactitude in the lines of his buildings. His art is an attempt to suggest the way we ordinarily experience these buildings in passing, rather than what we know them to be.
M.D.

Henri Joseph Harpignies

Born 1819 in Valenciennes; died 1916.

Son of a rich family who planned a commercial career for him, Harpignies decided instead, at the age of twenty-seven, to become a painter. He began his training in Paris in 1846 and was greatly influenced by the Barbizon school and especially by Corot, with whom he visited Italy in 1860. A painter of dark-toned landscapes, he was especially fond of woodland scenes.

19. A FARMHOUSE (1875)

Oil on canvas, 10-3/4 x 15-3/4 in. (27.3 x 40 cm.)
Signed, lower left: "H. Harpignies"

REFERENCES

D. Hannema, *Catalogue of the H. E. Ten Cate Collection* (1955), I, no. 72, p. 54; II, pl. 52.

COLLECTIONS

H. E. Ten Cate, The Netherlands (sale, Sotheby's, London, 3 December 1958, no. 75, repr.);
Thomas Agnew and Sons, London (by 1959);
Robert Ellis Simon (1958);
The Norton Simon Inc. Foundation, Los Angeles (1969).

REMARKS

In this painting Harpignies has created a peaceful if somewhat stark landscape scene. We can identify the season, the weather, and even the time of day from specific clues in the painting. The light is clear and strong, the sky is blue, and the trees are green and thick; we can assume that it is summertime. Therefore, it is probably warm, and there is also very little wind because the reflections of the buildings in the water are unmarred by ripples. A lack of shadows indicates that it is near the middle of the day. It is more difficult to determine the locale of the scene, but the architecture of the little manor with its towers and slate roofs suggests central France, where we know that Harpignies often painted. Except for a boat moving slowly in the middle of the water, no activity is depicted. Since we are not guided into the scene by a road or path, as earlier painters would have been, or by being able to empathize with human figures engaged in work or play, we are induced to contemplate the painting with more attention to its abstract, formal qualities. Indeed, the tranquil mood of the landscape is more effectively conveyed by pictorial means than it could be by means of a narration. The lucid, geometrical shapes of the manor and its reflection in the water seem to create the strongest note of stability and calm in the scene. Harpignies learned to compose his paintings in this way principally from his study of the work of Corot and of the Barbizon painters. He always remained faithful to their conception of landscape painting which stressed working out of doors and recording a direct impression of nature. However, he objected to the Impressionists' neglect of tonal modulation.
M.S.

Eugène Boudin

Born 1824 in Honfleur; died 1898.

Biographical sketch in Volume I.

20. COTTAGE AND PASTURE ON (THE BANKS OF) THE TOUQUES (ca. 1860-65)
Oil on canvas, 15-1/2 x 21-1/4 in.
(39.4 x 54 cm.)
Signed, lower right: E. Boudin

REFERENCES
R. SCHMIT, *Eugène Boudin* (1973), I, p. 77, no. 242, repr.

COLLECTIONS
Gerard, Paris;
Diard, Orange (France);
Galerie Schmit, Paris;
Arthur Tooth and Sons, Ltd., London;
Norton Simon Inc Foundation, Los Angeles (1973).

REMARKS
Boudin's painting captures the rustic charm of the French countryside. The artist conveys an idyllic mood through his use of soft tonal harmonies as he blends the verdant tones of the pasture with the clear blue of the sky. The complete naturalness of the scene is emphasized by the languorously grazing animals and unassuming cottage on the right. Boudin has rendered the stillness of the moment, perpetuating the pastoral beauty of a warm summer day. In 1849, Boudin traveled to Belgium. There he copied landscapes by the Dutch masters who excelled at expressing the tranquility of nature. It is their mood of pastoral calm which he evokes in this work. Boudin particularly admired the seventeenth-century Dutch landscapists for their rendering of large-scale skies, but he hoped to achieve greater spontaneity in his own paintings. He asked, "Did the Dutch painters find the poetry in the clouds for which I search or the tendencies in the sky which I admire to the point of adoration?" (Jean-Aubrey, *Boudin*, p. 22.) Baudelaire praised Boudin's skill at capturing atmospheric effects, claiming that one could guess the season, the time, and the wind. His enthusiasm was well-founded, as Boudin was to become the acknowledged master of skies in French painting. Boudin's genius for permeating his canvases with soft, luminous light was lauded by generations of artists and provided a source of inspiration for the Impressionists.
D.S.

21. OLD FISH MARKET IN BRUSSELS. 1871

Oil on panel, 9-1/2 x 13-1/4 in. (24 x 33.7 cm.)
Inscribed and dated, lower left: "Bruxelles 1871"
Signed, lower right: "E Boudin"

REFERENCES

R. SCHMIT, *Eugène Boudin* (1973), I, no. 644, repr.

EXHIBITIONS

Brussels, Palais des Beaux-Arts, "Les Peintres de la Mer," 1952.
Ghent, Musée des Beaux-Arts, "La Peinture dans les collections Gantoises," 1953, no. 28.
London, Marlborough Fine Arts Gallery, "A Tribute to Paul Maze: The Painter and His Time," 1967, no. 42.
Portland, Portland Art Museum, "Recent Acquisitions by the Norton Simon, Inc. Museum of Art," November 1968-March 1969, no. 1.
Princeton, New Jersey, The Art Museum, Princeton University, "Selections from the Norton Simon, Inc. Museum of Art," 2 December 1972-June 1974, no. 27, repr.

COLLECTIONS

Roland Leten;
Marlborough Alte und Moderne Kunst;
Norton Simon Inc Foundation, Los Angeles (1968).

REMARKS

Painted on a trip to Brussels in 1870, this picture reveals Boudin's fascination with everyday scenes. He focuses his full attention on the fish market by giving the sky and surrounding buildings a minimal place in his composition and captures the activity of the scene with short, quick brushstrokes which echo the movement of the market place. An exotic variety of sea life is displayed on the tables tended by the fishsellers. Boudin has placed the crowd of shoppers to the left of this colorful scene in order not to distract from his carefully arranged marine still lifes. The point of view and dark tones of this painting at first seem to contradict Boudin's professed interests in light, weather, and open space. However, closer examination of his rapid, broken brushwork reveals his preoccupation with movement and change. Here Boudin has modified his fascination with the panorama of nature and the constantly changing skies. He has focused on the activity and bustle of the market which offered him an arena filled with color and constantly moving forms. Boudin stated, "Anything painted directly from nature and on the spot has always a force, power, and vivacity of touch that one cannot find in the studio. . . ." (Jean-Aubry, *Boudin*, p. 155.) He frequently traveled with small wooden panels of the size used here, which were easily portable. They enabled him to rapidly set up his easel and paint directly what was moving before his eyes.
D.S.

22. FIGURES ON THE BEACH. 1886

Oil on canvas, 20 x 24 in. (50.8 x 60.9 cm.)
Signed and dated, lower left: "E. Boudin -86"

REFERENCES

R. Schmit, *Eugène Boudin* (1973), II, p. 319, no. 2148, repr.

EXHIBITIONS

Paris, Ecole des Beaux-Arts, "Exposition des oeuvres d'Eugène
Boudin," 9-30 January 1899, no. 84.

COLLECTIONS

Belvalette, Paris;
Brosset Heckel, Lyon (sale, Hôtel Drouot, Paris, 18 November
1966, no. 14, repr.);
Stephen Hahn, New York;
The Norton Simon Foundation, Los Angeles (1967).

REMARKS

Boudin, like the Impressionists, was interested in depicting ordinary people doing ordinary things. In this
work he represents groups of people digging for clams.
Yet, the figures are almost incidental, no more than
sign posts in a pictorial complex where the primary
focus is on the movements of nature. The vast, cloud-
laden sky fills two-thirds of the canvas and is reflected
in the tide pool on the right. The arc formed by this
still body of water works in counterpoint to the horizontal expanse of the sky and directs the viewer's attention to the activities of the clam diggers. But these
sketchily rendered figures are mere silhouettes in a
composition which stresses the subtle, ever-changing
relationship between sky and sea. Boudin masterfully
evokes the transitory weather patterns of the Normandy
Coast through his use of cool blues and heavy greys. His
persistent study of the skies of his native Normandy
led to a virtuosity of brushstroke which enabled him to
transpose onto canvas, in a lucid watercolor-like fashion, the effect of floating clouds merging into beach
and sea. Throughout his long life, Boudin claimed he
found his greatest happiness in "following the clouds,
brush in hand, savouring the good salt air of the beaches
and seeing the tide rise." (Jean-Aubry, *Boudin*, pp.
96-100.)
D.S.

Adolphe Joseph Thomas Monticelli

Born 1824 in Marseilles; died 1886.

Of Italian descent, Monticelli studied with Rey and Auguste Aubert. He lived in his native city except for two sojourns to Paris in the 1840's and the 1860's. After 1870 he returned to Marseilles and worked quietly for the rest of his life. His intensely Romantic temperament was strongly influenced by Dias and Delacroix and by Rembrandt. A painter of landscapes, still lifes, portraits and nudes, he received little recognition during his lifetime. Later generations, from the Symbolists to the Fauves, would appreciate his unique achievement. Until Vincent van Gogh began painting in the 1880's, no one had used color so intensely. Indeed, he had a considerable influence on Van Gogh, who said: "I owe everything to Monticelli, who taught me the chromatics of color."

23. FLOWERS (ca. 1879)
Oil on panel, 24-1/2 x 19 in. (156.5 x 123.2 cm.)
Signed, lower right: "Monticelli"

REFERENCES
A. SHEON, "Monticelli and Van Gogh," *Apollo* (June 1967), p. 445, repr.

EXHIBITIONS
London, Lefevre Gallery, "XIX and XX Century French Paintings," 1967, no. 14.
Philadelphia, Philadelphia Museum of Art, "Recent Acquisitions by the Norton Simon, Inc. Museum of Art," 1969, no. 5.
Princeton, New Jersey, The Art Museum, Princeton University, "Selections from the Norton Simon, Inc. Museum of Art," 2 December 1972-June 1974, no. 23, repr.

COLLECTIONS
D. Morley;
Lefevre Gallery, London (by 1967);
Norton Simon Inc Foundation, Los Angeles (1968).

REMARKS
This richly animated rendering of country flowers in a simple pot is a fine example of the lively interest in developing a free technique of thick impasto that interested several artists in the south of France in the 1860s and 1870s. The composition, rich palette, and heavy texture, in fact, call to mind contemporary flower-pieces by the young Cézanne. Monticelli has established a tone of somber richness in the choice of a dark wood panel for his background. This smooth surface serves as a foil for its content—thick pigments and color. Here and there the artist has allowed small areas of the brown wood to show through, adding variety and contrast. The green stocks and dark red poppies seem at times to withdraw into the panel. In contrast, the generous use of cream white for the daisies and roses suggests flowers emerging out of the shadows in an arc that bends from right to left toward the source of light. This application of white in daubs and swirls lends a sense of vitality to ordinary potted flowers. By rejecting a concern for the precise rendering of flowers and the delicate use of transparent paint in favor of virtuosity of expression and delight in textural pigment, Monticelli has broken with a dominant Parisian tradition. It was but a short step to the lighter palette and more intensely personalized vision of Van Gogh. T.C.

Henri Fantin-Latour

Born 1836 in Grenoble; died 1904.

Biographical sketch in Volume I.

24. A BUNCH OF MIXED ZINNIAS. 1881

Oil on canvas, 10 x 13-1/2 in. (25.4 x 34.3 cm.)
Signed and dated, top right: "Fantin '81"

REFERENCES

V. FANTIN-LATOUR, *Catalogue de l'oeuvre complet de Fantin-Latour* (1911), no. 1035.
D. HANNEMA, *Catalogue of the H. E. Ten Cate Collection* (1955), I, p. 51, no. 64.
P. and P. BRAME. (To be included in the forthcoming catalogue.)

COLLECTIONS

H. E. Ten Cate, The Netherlands (sale, Sotheby's, London, 3 December 1958, no. 57, repr.);
Thomas Agnew and Sons, London;
Robert Ellis Simon (1958);
The Norton Simon Foundation, Los Angeles (1969).

REMARKS

This work is a superb example of nineteenth-century still-life painting. Casually gathered together in a sketchily described container, the arrangement of zinnias inhabits a shallow, ambiguous space. It rests on an undefined surface and is set before an unadorned backdrop, a compositional device of spare yet candid simplicity. The composition is filled and animated solely by the flowers; they emerge from the shadowy setting by virtue of their fresh pink, orange and yellow colors and by the artist's rigorous analysis of their individual parts. Described in a single stroke of his brush, each petal is given a tangible sense of relief and lifelike vitality. Fantin-Latour favored the genre of still life as well as that of portraiture because both shared an essential quality of immobility. He applied to both a unique intensity of observation which derived from his involvement in the "realist" movement of the mid-nineteenth century. While Fantin's flowerpieces largely hark back to the tradition of seventeenth-century still-life, this more personal facet of his artistic output anticipated the visual poetry of the late nineteenth-century Symbolist movement.
K.H.

Paul-Camille Guigou

Born 1834 in Villars, Vaucluse; died 1871.

The son of well-to-do parents, Guigou was placed in a school for notaries. At an early age, however, he forsook the study of documents to draw and paint the landscapes of his native environment. He was encouraged by the director of the *Ecole des Beaux-Arts* of Marseilles. From 1854, he exhibited regularly with the *Société Artistique des Bouches-du-Phone*, along with Couture, Jules Dupré, Monticelli and Millet. He visited Paris in 1856, and settled there in 1862. This did not mean that he forsook his beloved Provençal countryside. He returned frequently to paint its rivers and valleys. Later his love expanded to embrace the river valley of the Seine and the Loire. A shy and retiring man, Guigou was largely unknown to his contemporaries.

25. THE VILLAGE OF ST. PAUL ON THE DURANCE 1865

     Oil on canvas, 25-1/2 x 59-1/4 in. (64.8 x 150.5 cm.)

     Signed and dated, lower right: "Paul Guigou. 65"

EXHIBITIONS
Paris, Palais Galliera, "Tableaux Modernes-Sculptures,"
    3 December 1967, no. 30, repr. in color (as "Le village
    près de la rivière").

COLLECTIONS
Havard Collection, France;
Arthur Tooth and Sons, Ltd., London;
The Norton Simon Foundation, Los Angeles (1968).

REMARKS

In this painting it is midsummer; the land is parched and the grass brown. The river itself is low; the sandy bottom and rocks are exposed like primordial remains washed up on the sands of time, as are the low, rolling hills. There is a quality of eternity and stasis, and of man's intimate relationship with nature. The village of St. Paul-les-Durance, with its central position in the composition, is the ostensible subject of this painting, yet it is practically lost within the flanking hills, the foliage, shadows, and reflections. Guigou's architectonic composition, however, reflects his interest in the horizon and the village seen as the compositional focal point. The vantage point is unusually low: the eye sweeps up to the town. The effect is cinematic, almost as if the curvature of the earth had been captured by wide-angle lens photography or viewed through a concave glass. The colors are deep, the blues of the sky and water are slightly muted, descriptive and natural. The technique is traditional, yet the point of view is strikingly modern. Particularly arresting is Guigou's handling of light. It is a clear day; no visible atmosphere affects our view of the scene. The details are crisp from foreground to background. As the years passed, perhaps the most significant change in Guigou's work was an increasingly personal conception of nature. Earlier works are generally smaller, less monumental, and technically more traditional than the later ones. This painting's size suggests that Guigou considered it an important statement of his intentions as a landscapist. In its stark grandeur and geometric clarity, Guigou has captured the essential character of this region by the simplest of pictorial means—without embellishment or exoticism.
R.A.

26. LANDSCAPE IN MARTIGUES

Oil on canvas, 11 x 18-1/4 in. (28 x 46.4 cm.)

COLLECTIONS

Arthur Tooth and Sons, Ltd., London;
Norton Simon Inc Foundation, Los Angeles (1973).

REMARKS

In this tranquil image of Martigues, a Mediterranean inlet just west of Marseilles, Guigou depicted a favorite motif—a road receding obliquely into the landscape. His small canvas is almost equally divided between sky, land and water. A woman with a basket on her head walks down the road toward us; sailboats and a town composed of tiny cubic buildings cling to the horizon. A few seagulls drift through the sky. Man and nature co-exist peacefully. It is a hot clear day in Martigues. The sun blazes, the atmosphere is dry, and the colors are intense and highly keyed—blues of sea and sky, browns of earth, and dark greens of the foliage. Deep shadows punctuate the road, cross the sea at the horizon and unobtrusively bring geometric clarity to the scene. They create a clearly defined foreground, middleground and background within a precise and ordered sense of recession. These devices reveal Guigou's intentions. His approach to landscape painting stresses the architectonic qualities of the site—the topographical, descriptive, and intellectual. His aim was total spatial and compositional clarity. Guigou's concern with light effects relates his art to that of other French landscape painters of the nineteenth century. Certain artists chose to interpret nature, usually the cooler, moister climes of northern and central France, through an atmospheric haze; others dematerialized reality through the use of discrete and disconnected brush strokes. Guigou did not, and undoubtedly his clear and luminous vision derived in part from the climate and topography of Provence.
R.A.

Jean Baptiste Armand Guillaumin

Born 1841 in Moulins; died 1927.

Primarily self-taught, he came to Paris at the age of sixteen and attended the *Académie Suisse* where he met his life-long friend, Pissarro. He participated in the *Salon des Réfusés* in 1863, and had three landscapes in the first Impressionist exhibition of 1874. He continued to exhibit with the Impressionists regularly, but that brought in very little money; he and Pissarro painted blinds to eke out a living. Guillaumin was a good friend of most of the Impressionists and many of the major Post-Impressionists. Although he was not the artistic revolutionary he thought himself to be, he was a sensitive painter of considerable talent in whose quietly lyrical style is reflected the principal historical achievements of his time.

27. POINT DU JOUR. 1874
    Oil on canvas, 21 x 25 in. (53 x 63.5 cm.)
    Signed and dated, lower left:
    "A Guillaumin 5.74"

REFERENCES
G. SERRET and D. FABIAN, *Armand Guillaumin: Catalogue raisonné de l'oeuvre peint* (1971), no. 33.

EXHIBITIONS
Princeton, New Jersey, The Art Museum, Princeton University, "Selections from the Norton Simon, Inc. Museum of Art," 2 December 1972-June 1974, no. 28, repr.

COLLECTIONS
Bernheim-Jeune, Paris;
Georges Hoentschel;
Mme Hoentschel de Malherbe (sale, Sotheby's, London, 24 April 1968, no. 94);
Norton Simon Inc Foundation, Los Angeles (1968).

REMARKS
The setting for this picture, by an artist who specialized in scenes along the Parisian quays, is a quiet residential section at the edge of the expanding metropolis. We look up the Seine toward the center of the city. In the distance on the other side of the river we see the looming smokestacks of industry—perhaps those of the burgeoning iron foundries. The Seine at this time was not only the major commercial artery, but a popular place for recreation as well. Moored in the middle distance is what appears to be a terminus for the passenger boat which plied the river, as well as a floating bathhouse or swimming school. However, we do not witness a scene of pleasure such as those Guillaumin's friends, the Impressionists, were to paint farther down the river at Argenteuil. Only the solitary boatman rowing toward the center of the river offers a sign of human activity in the direction of recreation. The people in this somber and curiously disquieting scene seem to concern the artist only as compositional elements and scale referrents—as vertical units or ciphers which are echoed in the lampposts, flagpole and smokestacks. Black smoke belching from the chimneys plays a larger role in pictures by Guillaumin than in the work of the other Impressionists who, for the most part, eschewed industrial motifs. One reason for the prominent role given this industrial pollutant is an aesthetic one: the billowing dark clouds create a striking visual contrast to the fleecy white ones that are a by-product of nature. We have no record of whether Guillaumin regarded these inevitable consequences of industrialization with disfavor.
M.D.

Stanislas Lépine

Born 1835 in Caen; died 1892.

Biographical sketch in Volume I.

28. PONT DE L'ESTACADE, PARIS (ca. 1885)
Oil on canvas, 10-1/4 x 15-3/4 in. (26 x 40 cm.)
Dedicated and signed, lower left: "à M. de
Fourcade, S. Lépine."

EXHIBITIONS
Princeton, New Jersey, The Art Museum, Princeton
University, "Selections from the Norton Simon, Inc.
Museum of Art," 2 December 1972-June 1974, no. 29,
repr.

COLLECTIONS
M. de Fourcade;
Galerie Schmit, Paris;
Norton Simon Inc Foundation, Los Angeles (1969).

REMARKS
In this small canvas the artist creates a portrait of the everyday aspect of the Seine—a view of the rough timber *estacade* or breakwater bridge that combed the currents of the Seine as they broke around the head of the Ile de Saint Louis. Lépine gives this simple bridge of pilings a subtle role as a screen that frames the single passageway to the channel beyond, through which the eye may travel along with the puffing canal barge. The figures in the foreground rest on the quay of the Port-aux-Vins, idly contemplating the passing river. The port docks are deserted for the day, and the empty loading planks are converted into Sunday fishing piers. Beyond the bridge and traffic of the Seine we see the mansard roofs of the Right Bank and the chestnut trees that line the Quai Henri IV in thick summer foliage. Lépine's palette of light, fresh tones combining tans and blues captures the diffuse light of the sun filtering through clouds. Violet and cream shades are reflected in the beach sand, while the softened rays pick out orange and tan among the greys of the clustered buildings. His brushwork is quick and unlabored, with simple thin strokes defining outlines in the cityscape and soft smudges creating the mass of foliage along the quay and the smoke of the barge. Lépine found delight in such simple activities along the Seine. He made himself the portraitist of its quais and bridges. He painted several larger versions of *L'Estacade*, one of which was singled out at the Paris Universal Exposition of 1885. This was one of the few public accolades of his work. (Couper, *Lépine*, p. 72.)
G.J.

29. FIGURES IN A COURTYARD

Oil on canvas, 17-1/2 x 12-1/2 in. (44.5 x 31.8 cm.)
Signed, lower left: "S. Lépine"

REFERENCES

P. WILSON (ed.), *Art at Auction* (1967), p. 48 repr.

COLLECTIONS

Sir Chester Beatty, Dublin (sale, Sotheby's, London, 28 June 1967, no. 1);
The Norton Simon Foundation, Los Angeles (1967).

REMARKS

Lépine presents an intimate view of this narrow courtyard in an enclosing perspective of subtly receding verticals. The sandy path framed by close, inward-leaning trees channels the eye from the woman with a basket to the less clearly defined couple sharing a conversation in the shadow of the far entryway. The man and woman seen in profile are almost miniatures in relation to the solitary woman in the courtyard, yet they retain interest as mysterious background elements. Cool, limpid colors portray a moist northern environment. The peaked slate roof could suggest Caen, Lépine's birthplace in Normandy, or the Ile-de-France, where he resided most of his life. Lépine may have taken his subject from the Chateau d'Orrouy, the country estate of his supportive admirer, Comte Doria, who provided him with a place to paint during his frequent Sunday visits. Lépine emphasizes the overgrown foliage in the courtyard with feathery brushwork similar to that of his former teacher, Corot. The scene, sheltered by the dappled arch of the framing trees, draws the viewer into a veiled intimacy.
G.J.

Pierre Puvis de Chavannes

Born 1824 in Lyons; died 1898.

Son of an engineer, he studied for the same profession, but on a trip to Italy he decided to become a painter. Both the heated emotions of Delacroix and the cool linearity of Ingres and Couture helped him in his struggle to develop an art based on the articulation of ideas, rather than a replication of "Nature." His effort was not appreciated by the *Salon*. Inspired by the Italian tradition to try to re-create a monumental style of wall painting, he decorated many public buildings in France, the most famous work being the *Life of Sainte Geneviève* (1874-98) in the Panthéon of Paris. His allegorical content, the flatness of his "picture plane" and the abstract rhythms of his compositions were a distinct influence on a number of Post-Impressionists and/or Symbolists, including Denis, Gauguin, Maillol and Seurat.

30. MEETING OF SAINT GENEVIEVE AND SAINT GERMAIN. 1879

Oil on canvas (triptych):
Left: 53 x 32-1/4 in. (134.2 x 81.8 cm.)
Center: 53 x 35-1/4 in. (134.2 x 89.4 cm.)
Right: 52-3/4 x 32 in. (131.7 x 81.2 cm.)
Right panel, signed and dated, lower right: "P. Puvis de Chavannes '79"

REFERENCES
C. YRIARTE, "Le Salon de 1876," *Gazette des Beaux-Arts*, 13 (1876), pp. 692-95.
L. C., "Studies for the Childhood of St. Genevieve, Puvis de Chavannes," *Bulletin of the Art Institute of Chicago* (January 1924), pp. 117-20, repr.
"Chicago Art Institute Gets Mural Studies by Puvis de Chavannes," *Art News*, 23 (1924): I.
The Art Institute of Chicago, *A Guide to the Paintings in the Permanent Collection* (1925), pp. 55-57.
"A Sketch by Puvis de Chavannes," *Bulletin of the Minneapolis Institute of Arts* (1 March 1930), pp. 44-46; repr. p. 45.
The Art Institute of Chicago, *A Guide to the Paintings in the Permanent Collection* (1932), pp. 51-53.

EXHIBITIONS
Paris, Salon of 1876.
Brooklyn, The Brooklyn Museum, "Religious Painting: 15th-19th Century," 2 October-13 November 1956, no. 26.
Princeton, New Jersey, The Art Museum, Princeton University, "Selections from the Norton Simon, Inc. Museum of Art," 2 December 1972-June 1974, no. 25, repr.

COLLECTIONS
Mr. and Mrs. James Byron;
Durand-Ruel, Paris;
The Art Institute of Chicago;
E. and A. Silberman Galleries, New York;
Huntington Hartford Collection, Gallery of Modern Art, New York;
Hirschl and Adler Galleries, New York;
Norton Simon Inc Foundation, Los Angeles (1968).

REMARKS
Respected in academic circles and by radical artists as well, Puvis made his reputation with his first state commission for the Panthéon in Paris. By selecting Genevieve's meeting with Saint Germain, he contributed to unifying the political and religious factions of the time which disputed whether the Panthéon should be the church of Saint Genevieve or a national monument to the heroes of France. As the triptych's caption explains, Genevieve was recognized and promised to God by Saint Germain in 429 A.D. when he and Saint Loup paused in Nanterre midway in their journey to England to fight a heresy. The meeting was significant, for the older saint's blessing presaged Genevieve's destiny as the savior of her fellow French citizens in the siege of Paris by Attilla, which qualified her as a heroine of France's early history. Genevieve is surrounded by villagers of all ages, representing a cross-section of traditional French crafts and livelihoods. The scene also symbolized the saint's religious importance during the siege as a protective shepherdess—a Christian guardian of the needy. Puvis's straightforward, frieze-like arrangement of his figures across the foreground of the triptych lends his narrative a readability and economy of means which was one of the artist's primary contributions to the art of his time. Puvis abandoned the traditional illusionistic values of violent contrasts of light and shadow, deep spatial recession, and radical foreshortening of his figures in his monumental compositions. Through a uniform simplification of form as well as a consistent use of subdued pastel color, Puvis sought to flatten the illusion of depth of his compositions, making them more consonant with the wall surface and compatible with their location. This abstract conception of form, drawn from his enchantment with the masters of fifteenth-century Florentine fresco painting, was one of the artist's primary contributions to the origins of modern art. This triptych is a reduced but faithful replica of the three principal sections of the Panthéon decorations which were exhibited in the *Salon* of 1876 and installed in 1878.
K.H.

Edgar Degas

Born 1834 as Hilaire Germain Degas de Gas in Paris;
died 1917.

Biographical sketch in Volume I.

31. WOMAN COMBING HER HAIR BEFORE A MIRROR (ca. 1877)

Oil on canvas, 15-1/2 x 12-1/2 in. (39.3 x 31.7 cm.)
Stamped signature of the Degas *vente*, lower right: "Degas"

REFERENCES

P.-A. LEMOISNE, *Degas et son oeuvre* (1946), II, no. 436.
AMERICAN ART GALLERIES, *The Notable Private Collection of Paintings and Pastels by Hilaire Germaine Edgar Degas formed by Jacques Seligmann of Paris* (1921), no. 24.

EXHIBITIONS

San Francisco, California Palace of the Legion of Honor, *"Man: Glory, Jest and Riddle,"* 10 November 1964-3 January 1965, no. 168.
Princeton, New Jersey, The Art Museum Princeton University, "Selections from the Norton Simon, Inc. Museum of Art," 2 December 1972-June 1974, no. 38, repr.

COLLECTIONS

Estate of the artist (sale, Galerie Georges Petit, Paris, 6-8 May 1918 no. 31);
Jacques Seligmann (sale, American Art Galleries, New York, 27 January 1921 no. 24);
Tannhauser;
M. Knoedler & Co., New York (by 1964);
Norton Simon Inc Foundation, Los Angeles (1968).

REMARKS

The theme of woman caught in a moment of self-absorption is persistent in Degas's art. Here the artist presents the viewer with an intimate and unusual look at a young woman alone in a room with her own reflected image. Degas himself compares scenes such as this to looking through a keyhole. This voyeuristic effect is increased by the way the painter handles the left and lower edges of the canvas: the vigorous, almost desultory, brushwork obscures these areas, creating the suggestion of an opening through which we watch. This work has an almost photographic quality in the way the figure is put into soft focus while the area around her is left unfocused. The woman's face is generalized to such an extent that we get little sense of her as an individual. The soft and delicate brushstrokes of the face and arms contrast strongly with the casual, calligraphic strokes which cover the rest of the painting. A quiet grey tonality, broken only by the red with which the lips are painted, enhances the meditative calm of the scene. Though certain of Degas's contemporaries such as Huysmans thought the painter's candid views of women expressed hatred and contempt for them, there is little evidence to suppose that this was his attitude at all. Yet the central paradox of his art remains. He has brought us closer to the ordinarily unseen daily activities of women than any other artist before, but at the same time his work exhibits an unprecedented psychological remoteness from his model as a human personality.
M.D.

32. GRAND ARABESQUE, FIRST TIME
(c.1882/85)

Bronze, H: 19 in. (48.3 cm.)
Signed, on base, top front: "Degas"
Stamped "H E R; Cire Perdue,
    A. A. Hebrard"

REFERENCES

J. REWALD, *Degas: Sculpture, The Complete Works* (1956),
    p. 148, pl. 37.

EXHIBITIONS

Princeton, New Jersey, The Art Museum, Princeton
    University, "Selections from the Norton Simon, Inc.
    Museum of Art," 2 December 1972-June 1974, no. 79, repr.

COLLECTIONS

Degas Family;
Stephen Hahn Gallery, New York;
Norton Simon Inc Foundation, Los Angeles (1968).

REMARKS

In the small bronze statuette, Degas demonstrates his fascination with the female nude figure caught in a fleeting movement. In his figure sculptures, the analysis of the movement of the subject and the accommodation of the body to form the movement were always his first concerns. In contrast to his painting, he did not in his sculpture seek to capture the mood of the setting or the individuality of the model. In "Grande Arabesque" the face is anonymous, the features suggested rather than defined. The movement or posture of the dancer's body, however, is caught as it turns towards the right, the left leg and hip slightly raised, the torso thrust forward and to the right to balance the movement, and the right arm raised to point the direction, while the left is partially lowered to emphasize the final continuance of the turn. W.H.E.

33. DANCERS IN PINK (ca. 1883)
Pastel on cardboard, 28-1/2 x 15-1/2 in. (72.4 x 38.7 cm.)

REFERENCES

P. Lafond, *Degas* (1919), II, repr. opp. p. 30.
P.-A. Lemoisne, *Degas et son oeuvre* (1946), II, no. 486, repr. p. 269.

EXHIBITIONS

New York, Jacques Seligmann Galleries, "The Stage," 1939, no. 20, repr.
Cleveland, Cleveland Museum of Art, "In Memoriam: Leonard C. Hanna, Jr.," 1958, no. 12, repr.

COLLECTIONS

Henri Lerolle, Paris;
Hector Brame, Paris;
Durand-Ruel, Paris;
Jacques Seligmann and Co., Inc., Paris;
Leonard C. Hanna, Jr., Cleveland;
E. V. Thaw and Co., Inc., New York;
The Norton Simon Foundation, Los Angeles (1969).

REMARKS

In this painting Degas presents a charming scene from a ballet. The dancers are on stage in costume in front of a painted landscape backdrop. However, it is impossible to tell what ballet is being performed. Instead of showing the full stage, Degas has chosen to limit his presentation to only two of the dancers. We know that there is at least one other dancer on stage by the very small section of a cut-off skirt which can be seen on the right edge of the picture. A constant experimenter, Degas was one of the first modern artists to bring into his art the techniques and even the spirit of Japanese painting, such as oblique views and the use of empty space for creative effects. Here not only is the scene chopped off in a seemingly arbitrary manner, but Degas has also employed the unusual viewpoint of depicting the women from the back, depersonalizing them in the process. In the picture these visual devices are skillfully combined with Degas's mastery of composition and color; he has created a harmonious, flowing rhythm in which all elements of the painting are brought together through repeated, curving lines. The position of each dancer's left arm echoes the sweep of the braids, the tilt of the heads, the form of the tutus, and the branches of the tree. The delicate movements of the dance are conveyed through Degas's subtle use of pastel colors. Pink pervades everything, even the arms and faces of the two dancers, while the blue outlines and areas of turquoise and chartreuse help to contrast with and further emphasize the primary tone. In the painting by Renoir, "Au Piano," which represents the studio of Henri Lerolle, this pastel is on the wall.
J.B.

34. THE IRONERS (ca. 1884)

Oil on canvas, 32-1/4 x 29-1/2 in. (81.9 x 74.9 cm.)
Signed, lower left: "Degas"

REFERENCES

P. FECHTER, "Die Sammlung Schmitz," *Kunst und Künstler*, 8 (1909-10), p. 22.
L. HOURTICQ, "Edgar Degas," *Art et Décoration* (1912), p. 106.
K. SCHEFFLER, "Die Sammlung Oscar Schmitz in Dresden," *Kunst und Künstler*, 19 (1920-21), p. 186.
A. VOLLARD, *Degas* (1924), pl. 114.
O. SCHURER, "Internationale Kunstausstellung, Dresden," *Deutsche Kunst und Dekoration* (1927), p. 273.
J. B. MANSON, *Life and Work of Edgar Degas* (1927), p. 52.
E. WALDMANN, *Die Kunst des Realismus und des Impressionismus in XIX Jahrhundert* (1927), p. 97, pl. 484.
A. RUBENSTEIN, *Catalogue de la collection Oscar Schmitz* (1936), p. 57.
C. MAUCLAIR, *Degas* (1941), p. 104.
P.-A. LEMOISNE, *Degas et son oeuvre* (1946), II, no. 687.
D. W. STEADMAN, "The Norton Simon Exhibition at Princeton," *Art Journal* (Fall 1972), pp. 34-40; repr. in color on cover.

EXHIBITIONS

Dresden, "Internationale Kunstausstellung," 1926.
Zurich, Kunsthaus, "Oscar Schmitz Collection," 1932, no. 23.
Princeton, New Jersey, The Art Museum, Princeton University, "Selections from the Norton Simon Museum of Art," 2 December 1972-June 1974, no. 40, repr. in color.

COLLECTIONS

Oscar Schmitz;
Chester A. Beatty;
Arthur Tooth and Sons, London;
Norton, Lucille Ellis, and Robert Ellis Simon (1959);
Norton Simon and The Norton Simon Foundation (1969);
Norton Simon Inc. Foundation, Los Angeles (1971).

REMARKS

In this painting Degas portrays the reality of the working-class life of two launderesses caught unobserved. He is primarily interested in studying the movement of the two women's bodies. He contrasts the straining effort of the woman on the right with the brief relaxation of the woman on the left, both exhausted by the continual work of the laundry. The woman on the right is completely involved in the demanding labor, her body bent forward to concentrate her entire weight and strength in a pressing movement on the iron as she works on a shirt. Her face is in shadow and she becomes an almost indistinguishable figure, her identity obscured by the routine difficulty of her work and life. The woman on the left raises one arm to stretch her tired body—her yawn an expression not only of exhaustion, but of the boredom resulting from the monotonous labor she must perform. Her features, plain and rough, are the only aspects of her figure which differentiate her from her companion. This woman with her bottle is not an absinthe drinker; the bottle could be filled with a refreshment or with water to sprinkle onto the shirts. The three light-colored and vaguely defined areas in the background are also ambiguous. They seem to be patches of hanging laundry. The woman on the left is centrally framed against the left-hand patch. The ironing woman bridges the gap between the two other sheets which aids in defining her half of the composition. This painting is one in a series of similar pictures of Ironers. These variations of the same scene or theme are not at all unusual for Degas. He was seldom satisfied with a completed painting and would repeatedly rework themes and pictures.

J.B.

35. DANCE REHEARSAL IN THE FOYER
(1885)

Oil on canvas, 34-7/8 x 37-3/4 in. (89 x 96 cm.)
Stamped signature of the Degas sale, lower right:
"Degas"

REFERENCES
R. FLINT, "Private Collection of Joseph Stransky," *Art News,*
(1931), pp. 87-88.
P.-A. LEMOISNE, *Degas et son oeuvre* (1946), III, p. 470, no. 819,
repr. p. 471.

EXHIBITIONS
Portland, Portland Art Museum, "Recent Acquisitions by the
Norton Simon, Inc. Museum of Art," November 1968-
March 1969, no. 4.

COLLECTIONS
Estate of the artist (sale, Galerie Georges Petit, Paris,
6-8 May 1918, no. 66);
Durand-Ruel, Paris;
Joseph Hessel;
Josef Stransky;
Mrs. Pierre Matisse;
Norton Simon Inc Foundation, Los Angeles (1968).

REMARKS
In this painting Degas invites the viewer to enter the
working world of the ballet, depicting a rehearsal which
takes place in one of the practice rooms of the newly
constructed Parisian opera house. As they recede into
the background, the dancers become less distinct. The
positions of the four front dancers are carefully delineated, but it is impossible to ascertain exactly what pose
or even how many women actually appear in the background. The two dancers on the left, who appear to
have been painted twice, show the lines of former place-
ments which Degas chose to leave. Looking closely at
areas on the left of the painting, such as the window's
edge or the skirt of the dancer farthest to the left, one
can see thumb prints along with brushstrokes. This un-
expected technique of modeling with paint may presage
the artist's later interest in the techniques of modeling
wax in his sculpture which he allegedly began when his
eyes failed in the 1880s. The faceless, anonymous dancers that Degas used as models were mainly girls from
the working class who were enrolled in the ballet school
at an early age, more often for reasons of employment
than art. These women, who spent many hours each day
at the demanding training, were known as the "rats"
of the Opéra. In contemporary literature and art they
were often portrayed as innocent or willing victims of
upperclass gentlemen who frequented the practice ses-
sions hoping to compromise their virtue. This scene is a
rare depiction of the circular training room at the top
of the Opéra building, identifiable by its round win-
dows. The painting, however, probably was not executed on the spot since Degas did all his work in his
studio, sometimes from preliminary sketches, but primarily from memory and models.
J.B.

36. WOMAN RUBBING HER BACK WITH
A SPONGE, TORSO (ca. 1885-1890)
Bronze, H: 17 in. (43.2 cm.)
Signed, lower right leg: "Degas"
Numbered and stamped, lower left leg: "28
HER. D, CIRE PERDUE A. A.
HEBRARD"

REFERENCES

J. REWALD, *Degas: Sculpture, The Complete Works* (1956),
no. LI, p. 153, pl. 80.

EXHIBITIONS

Princeton, New Jersey, The Art Museum, Princeton
University, "Selections from the Norton Simon, Inc.
Museum of Art," 2 December 1972-June 1974, no. 80,
repr.

COLLECTIONS

Degas Family;
Private Collection, Paris;
Paul Rosenberg & Co., New York;
Norton Simon Inc Foundation, Los Angeles (1968).

REMARKS

Woman Rubbing her Back with a Sponge, like *Grande Arabesque* is also a study of the female nude figure caught in
fragmentary motion. Here, however, the anonymity of
the subject is even greater, for Degas sacrifices not only
one arm but the most identifiable portion of the human
body, the head and face. In compensation for these
losses, he has created in the figure a particularly rich
composition of curvilinear mass and form. The torso
itself bends gracefully to the left while the right arm
is tautly pulled to the right and rear, creating by its
tension the balance for the mass of the torso.
W.H.E.

37. WOMAN DRYING HER HAIR

(ca. 1905-07)
Pastel on paper, 28 x 24-1/2 in. (71.1 x
62.2 cm.)
Stamped signature of the Degas *vente*, lower
right: "Degas"

REFERENCES

P.-A. LEMOISNE, *Degas et son oeuvre* (1946), III, no. 1454.

EXHIBITIONS

Paris, Galerie Durand-Ruel, "Edgar Degas," 1960, no. 63.
Princeton, New Jersey, The Art Museum, Princeton
University, "Selections from the Norton Simon, Inc.
Museum of Art," 2 December 1972-June 1974, no. 41, repr.

COLLECTIONS

Estate of the artist (sale, Galerie Georges Petit, Paris,
11-13 December 1918, no. 134);
Ambroise Vollard;
Durand-Ruel, Paris;
Sam Salz;
Private Collection, New York;
Sam Salz;
Alex Reid and Lefevre Gallery;
Norton Simon Inc Foundation, Los Angeles (1969).

REMARKS

This intimate picture is rendered in pastel, a medium
in which Degas was a great innovator and consummate
master. The theme is one the artist depicted many
times—a woman fresh from her tub combing her hair.
This familiar, everyday scene seems strange, almost un-
recognizable, because of the pose the painter chose to
capture. We must study it closely to understand the
anatomy. Degas has intentionally confounded our ex-
pectations by the placement of the woman's left leg.
This impossibly positioned leg is where we would ordinarily find her right arm. The artist has obscured the
contour of her breast and used hatching of the same
quality and intensity for both her right side and distant
leg; the result is that we tend to read the side closest to
us and both her legs as being in the same plane. Her
right arm is raised and partially hidden under the large
towel. Her face and her personality, apparently of no
consequence to the artist, are totally obscured. The
thick hatching which covers the whole surface of the
paper is characteristic of the work of Degas's later years.
As these strokes show only casual concern for following
the contour of the woman's body, and since her body
and the background are treated with the same heavy,
vertical strokes, the whole picture is flattened, making
it a surface upon which the artist is free to display his
bravura technique with the pastel crayon. This surface
reveals the artist's skill at harmonizing bright, primary
colors and his belief that shadows, which are tinted
green and purple here, should be colored. That this
depiction of a woman at her toilet, totally devoid of
anecdote and showing no regard for the individual
character of the model, could be considered a significant
work of art was something Degas himself recognized as
a new development in Western painting, for he con-
fided that earlier in the nineteenth century he would
have painted Susanna and the Elders.
M.D.

Claude Oscar Monet

Born 1840 in Paris; died 1926.

Biographical sketch in Volume I.

38. MOUTH OF THE SEINE AT HONFLEUR. 1865

Oil on canvas, 35-1/2 x 59 in. (90.2 x 149.9 cm.)
Signed and dated, lower right: "Claude Monet 1865"

REFERENCES

(Pigalle), *L'Autographe au Salon de 1865 et dans les ateliers*, 9 (24 June 1865), p. 76 (with pen drawing).
P. Mantz, "Salon de 1865," *Gazette des Beaux-Arts*, 7e anée, XIX (July 1865), p. 26.
G. Privat, *Place aux jeunes: Causeries critiques sur le Salon de 1865* (1865), p. 190.
E. Bricon, *Psychologie d'art* (1900), p. 297-298.
W. Dewhurst, *Impressionist Painting—Its Genesis and Development* (1904), p. 39.
T. Duret, *Histoire des peintres impressionnistes* (1906), p. 95, 101 (1939 ed. p. 70, 76).
G. Geffroy, *Claude Monet* (1922), pp. 27-28.
C. Mauclair, *Claude Monet* (1924), p. 6 (1943), p. 8.
R. Régamey, "Formation de Claude Monet," *Gazette des Beaux Arts* (February 1927), p. 76.
M. de Fels, *La Vie de Claude Monet* (1929), p. 73.
C. Léger, *Claude Monet* (1930), p. 6.
X. Lathom, *Claude Monet* (1935), p. 46-47.
G. Mack, *Paul Cézanne* (1935), p. 187.
G. Grappe, *Claude Monet* (n.d.) pp. 16, 17, 18.
A. Tabarant, *La Vie artistique au temps de Baudelaire* (4th ed.) (1942), p. 425.
M. Malingue. *Claude Monet* (1943), p. 15.
G. Bazin, *L'Epoque impressionniste* (1947), p. 10 (1953 ed., p. 26).
J. Robiquet, *L'Impressionnisme vecu* (1948), p. 62.
J. Cassou, *Les Impressionnistes et leur époque* (1953), p. 17 (1956 ed., p. 17).
F. Mathey, *L'Impressionnisme* (1956), p. 37.
R. Th. Stoll, *La Peinture impressionniste* (1957), p. 40 (Zurich ed., 1957, p. 44).
C. Monet, "The Artist as a Young Man," *Art News Annual*, XXVI (1957), p. 198.
K. Kuh and W. Van der Rohe, "Homage to Claude Monet," *The Art Institute of Chicage Quarterly*, LI, 2 (1 April 1957), p. 28.
J. Letheve, *Impressionnistes et symbolistes devant la presse* (1959), pp. 29, 30.
W. C. Seitz, *Claude Monet* (1960), pp. 10, 16, 46, repr. p. 11, Fig. 5.
F. Mathey, *The Impressionists* (trans. by Jean Steinberg) (1961), pp. 62-63, 66.
J. Rewald, *The History of Impressionism* (1946), pp. 102, 106, 107, repr. p. 106.
R. Gimpel, *Journal d'un collectionneur, marchand de tableaux* (1963) pp. 253-254.
Y. Taillandier, *Monet* (1963), p. 93.
C. M. Mount, *Monet* (1966), pp. 76-77, 86, 87, 90, 91, 95-97, 403.

D. Wildenstein, "Claude Monet," *Kindlers Malerei Lexikon*, IV (1967), pp. 466, 470.
J. Isaacson, *Monet: Le Déjeuner sur l'herbe* (1972), pp. 20, 102, note 29.
L. R. Bortolatto, *L'opera completa di Claude Monet* (1972), p. 88, no. 6, repr. p. 88.
D. Wildenstein, *Claude Monet: catalogue raisonné* (in preparation).

EXHIBITIONS

Paris, Salon of 1865, no. 1524.
Paris, Galerie Durand-Ruel, "Claude Monet de 1865 à 1888," 1935, no. 1.
London, Arthur Tooth & Sons, Ltd., "Selected Pictures by Claude Monet," 12 March-4 April 1936, no. 19.
Paris, Galerie Durand-Ruel, "Claude Monet," 22 May-30 September 1959, no. 1, repr.

COLLECTIONS

Rouselle Collection;
MM. Bernheim-Jeune;
Georges Bernheim;
M. Y. de Saint Albin, Paris;
Wildenstein & Co., Inc., New York;
The Norton Simon Foundation, Los Angeles (1973).

REMARKS

This large painting was one of the young Monet's first entries in the Paris National Exhibition of 1865. Although the success of his Salon debut was to prove short-lived, his paintings were reviewed favorably. Monet continued his interest in the painting of water and the momentary effects of light and weather. The scenery around Honfleur was familiar to Monet, who had spent his childhood in Normandy. The highlighting of the background, while the middle and foreground remain in shadow (a device in seventeenth-century Dutch painting) is given a new force here. The influence of painters who studied clouds (Boudin among others) is evident in the freely sketched areas of brushwork and subdued greys of the sky. Yet, a rich overlay of white upon the clouds toward the middle of the picture, along with a bold use of cerulean blue, reveal a vigor and conception that was Monet's own. The force of the wind is captured in the sailboats' sweep to the right as they struggle against a current of choppy waves flowing in the opposite direction. A concern for overall impact rather than descriptive detail is revealed in the almost cursory depiction of the figures in the rowboat and the flock of seagulls hovering along the right side of the canvas. Monet's pursuit of unity of effect and tonal modulations is the most striking and remarkable feature of this important work. What Monet is doing is seeking a different kind of unity with techniques that have developed to a new level of abstraction.
M.H.R.

39. COAST OF NORMANDY. 1882

Oil on canvas, 23 x 31 in. (58 x 78.7 cm.)
Signed and dated, lower right: "Claude
Monet '82"

EXHIBITIONS

New York, Stephen Hahn Gallery, "Cliffs and the Sea," 1968.
Philadelphia, Philadelphia Museum of Art, "Recent
    Acquisitions by the Norton Simon, Inc. Museum of Art,"
    1969, no. 4.
Princeton, New Jersey, The Art Museum, Princeton
    University, "Selections from the Norton Simon, Inc.
    Museum of Art," 2 December 1972-June 1974, no. 30, repr.

COLLECTIONS

M. Knoedler and Co.;
Private Collection, United States (sale, Christie's, London,
    28 June 1968, no. 70);
Stephen Hahn Gallery, New York (by 1968);
Norton Simon Inc Foundation, Los Angeles (1968).

REMARKS

Monet selected for his vantage point in this scene the top of the grassy cliffs that overlook the beach with its large expanse of blue-green water. The high position of the horizon sets at a distance the slate blues and grays of the heavy cloud bank rolling in toward the coast. Both tonal harmonies and the overall unity of the painting have been established by an aqua underpainting of the ground of the canvas. Areas of land, sea, and sky assume simple organic patterns within the rectangle of the picture. This use of patterned landscape is similar to that of the Japanese printmakers whose works were widely admired by Monet and his circle. The absence of habitation helps create the somber mood cast by a long dark shadow spreading across the beach along the edge of the water. This shadow seems to re-emerge, somewhat ambiguously and in lighter tones, to form the shoreline along the horizon. The suggestion is of ebb tide receding to reveal a residue of seaweed and mussel-covered rocks. This mass of deepest violet is tightly woven together with shades of deep blues, greens and pink shot through with thick daubs of white which could represent residual tide pools. The shallow water of low tide is depicted with the softer tones of aqua along the seaward edges of the rocks, the palest mauve evoking the sand beneath. The windswept grasses of the foreground cliffs display an animated texture in striking contrast to the smooth calm of the sea. Grey areas of rock along the face of the cliff are enlivened with pinks and lavender interspersed with blues from the sky and greens from the grass below. The rapid calligraphy of the heavily pigmented brush only partially serves to delineate the earth. This energy and freedom of brushwork reveals a highly expressive interpretation of form which was to become even more evident in later years.
M.H.R.

Pierre Auguste Renoir

Born 1841 in Limoges; died 1919.

Biographical sketch in Volume I.

40. GIRL IN A YELLOW HAT (1885)
Oil on canvas, 26-1/4 x 21-5/8 in. (67 x 55.4 cm.)
Signed, lower left: "Renoir"

REFERENCES

A. VOLLARD, *Tableaux, pastels et dessins de Pierre Auguste Renoir*
(2 vols. 1918), I, p. 4, Fig. 13.
I. HOPPER, "Vollard and Stieglitz," *American Magazine of Art*,
36 (1933), p. 544.

EXHIBITIONS

New York, M. Knoedler & Co., "Paintings from the Ambroise
Vollard Collection," 1933, no. 27.
New York, Metropolitan Museum of Art, "Renoir: A Special
Exhibition of his Paintings," 1937, no. 43.
New York, Duveen Galleries, "Renoir," 1941, no. 55.
Newark, Newark Museum, "Owned in New Jersey," 1946,
no. 61.
New York City, Wildenstein & Co., Inc., "Renoir," 1950,
no. 50.
Newark, Newark Museum, "From the Collection of Mrs. C.
Suydam Cutting," 1954, no. 8.
New York City, Wildenstein & Co., Inc., "Renoir," 1958,
no. 47.
New York City, Wildenstein & Co., Inc., "Olympia's
Progeny," 1965, no. 42.
Philadelphia, Philadelphia Museum of Art, "Recent
Acquisitions by the Norton Simon, Inc. Museum of Art,"
1969, no. 11.
Princeton, New Jersey, The Art Museum, Princeton University,
"Selections from the Norton Simon, Inc. Museum of Art,"
2 December 1972-June 1974, no. 36, repr.

COLLECTIONS

Ambroise Vollard;
M. Knoedler & Co., New York;
Mrs. Charles Suydam Cutting;
Wildenstein and Co., Inc., New York;
Norton Simon Inc Foundation, Los Angeles (1969).

REMARKS

The sitter is Mlle. Lami, the daughter of the artist
Frank Lami. The painting is harmoniously colored and
thickly brushed with heavy pigment. In the background
the paint was mixed liberally with white, which shows
in streaks in the brushstrokes. Occasionally, especially
around the right shoulder and the edge of the hat, the
background encroaches upon the image of the girl. The
long strokes of blue and green paint merge into an
opalescent shimmer which contrasts strikingly with the
solid, quiet figure of the girl. The figure is painted with
the same long strokes of paint as the chair and the background. As a preliminary step she was outlined in
dark brown, but the outline was lost in subsequent paint
except around the fingers, face and hat. It appears that
the face was over-painted: thin white paint was applied on top of the flesh tone which is made up of
pinks, yellows, and blues. This painting evokes an
ambiguous impression for the spectator—that of a mixture of technical virtuosity and awkwardness. Some elements, such as the young lady's hat and the flowers,
show a treatment of volumes which could bring to
mind Cézanne or Van Gogh. However, the range of
colors, clear and almost acid, is a reflection of Renoir's
own fascination with color. The portraiture of women
remains one of the most interesting aspects of late
nineteenth-century French art.
R.L.

41. RECLINING NUDE (ca. 1890)

Oil on canvas, 13 x 16 in. (33.5 x 41 cm.)
Signed, lower right: "Renoir"

REFERENCES

J. G. GOULINAT, "Les Sources du Métier de Renoir,"
L'Art Vivant (1925), no. 72, p. 23.

EXHIBITIONS

Paris, Galerie Bernheim-Jeune, "Cinquante Renoirs," 1927,
no. 13.
Montreal, Galerie Hervé, "A. Renoir," 1967, no. 11.
Philadelphia, Philadelphia Museum of Art, "Recent
Acquisitions by the Norton Simon, Inc. Museum of Art,"
1969, no. 12.
Princeton, New Jersey, The Art Museum, Princeton
University, "Selections from the Norton Simon, Inc.
Museum of Art," 2 December 1972-June 1974, no. 37, repr.

COLLECTIONS

Galerie Bernheim-Jeune, Paris;
Olivier Saincere;
Farjon;
Stephen Hahn Gallery;
Norton Simon Inc Foundation, Los Angeles (1968).

REMARKS

Throughout Renoir's career, the pictorial description of the female nude served as a means by which he could explore the complex interaction between volume, tone, light and atmosphere, as expressed in vibrating color and palpable brushstrokes. During the 1870s, Renoir's characteristic style reflected the Impressionist's interest in the relationship between light and freely applied touches of color, resulting in the dissolution of formal boundaries. After 1880, this style no longer satisfied him, and beginning with a trip to Italy in 1881-2, he returned to a style of painting the nude which was more linearly controlled. From 1884 to 1887, Renoir painted and drew the nude with an overwhelming interest in formal definition, suppressing coloristic bravura. This matte, flattened style, deriving from Pompeian murals and Raphael's frescoes, permitted him to recapture the clarity of the human figure in sunlight, silhouetted against a landscape background and bounded by strong contour lines. After 1888 Renoir began once more to rely upon the principle of optical mixture of colors and to model his nudes with elongated, freely flowing brushstrokes, as in this painting of approximately 1890.
B.W.

42. WOMAN WITH A ROSE (c. 1916)

Oil on canvas, 32 x 25-1/2 in. (81.3 x 64.8 cm.)
Signed, lower left: "Renoir"

REFERENCES

J. MEIER-GRAEFE, *Renoir* (1929), p. 428, no. 390.
A. ANDRÉ and M. ELDER, *L'Atelier de Renoir,* II (1931), no. 529, p. 165.
The Connoisseur (American Edition) (August 1965), repr. in color on the cover.

EXHIBITIONS

Montreal, Galerie Hervé, "A Renoir," 1967.

COLLECTIONS

Private Collection, France (sale, Parke-Bernet, New York, 11 May 1953, no. 62, repr.);
P. Gerli, New York;
Acquavella Galleries, New York;
The Norton Simon Foundation, Los Angeles (1967).

REMARKS

This dark-eyed, dark-haired sitter resembles Gabrielle Renard, one of Renoir's favorite models. The soft modeling and smooth texture of her face and neck are set off by daubs of thick paint along the neckline of the blouse. Renoir frequently placed roses beside a woman's skin. This device brings to mind the traditional association of the rose with Venus as the Goddess of Love. In this instance, the relaxed young woman holds a reddish rose on her lap and another of pale yellow is held close to her ear. The single petal trailing along the side of her cheek calls attention to the freshness and delicate blush of both flower and flesh. The model is posed in a manner which activates a flow of long curves that sweep along and around the contours of the body. An affinity for earlier formal tradition is evident in the full-bodied proportions of the female form similar to those preferred by Venetian painters of the sixteenth century, Rubens and Boucher. Renoir's adherence to Impressionism shows in areas of hazy forms, colored shadows and flickering lights conveyed by a sumptuous use of broken color. Their range, however, is characteristic of the artist's palette after 1900 when his canvases were flooded with russet tones. The reddish cast of the flesh tones is reflected in shades of orange and yellow in the blouse as well as in the tints of the two roses. The tones and colors of the lower part of the figure approximate those of the background to such an extent that the form tends to dissolve below the knees. This, in combination with colored shadows that serve to emphasize the weight of the hip, creates in the lower portion of the figure a curious ambiguity of solidity and weightlessness.
M.R.

Auguste Rodin

Born 1840 in Paris; died 1917.

Biographical sketch in Volume I.

43. PAS-DE-DEUX B (ca. 1910-13)
Bronze, H: 13 in. (33 cm.)
(Edition of 12, cast of 12)
Signed and numbered on front figure's raised foot: "A Rodin, no. 12"
Stamped on right foot of front figure: "Georges Rudier, Fondeur, Paris"
Copyrighted on right foot of rear figure: "© by Musée Rodin 1966"

EXHIBITIONS
Princeton, New Jersey, The Art Museum, Princeton University, "Selections from the Norton Simon, Inc. Museum of Art," 2 December 1972-June 1974, no. 70, repr.

COLLECTIONS
Musée Rodin, Paris;
Norton Simon Inc Foundation, Los Angeles (1966).

REMARKS
Pas-de-Deux B is a study in the depiction of motion. The problem greatly challenged Rodin; he gave it much thought and exploration. Not content to capture the most transitory moment of the dance, he strove to achieve a continuity of movement. In *Pas-de-Deux B* as in other related studies, the sculptor has roughly and rapidly molded the clay to reflect the tempo of the dance. In this small work, however, Rodin has gone one step further by showing the same dancer twice in the same study, with the second figure in a slightly advanced point of the dance so that we see a progression rather than a frozen moment.
W.H.E.

Paul Cézanne

Born 1839 in Aix-en-Provence; died 1906.

Biographical sketch in Volume I.

44. UNCLE DOMINIQUE (1865-67)
Oil on canvas, 18 x 15 in. (46 x 38 cm.)

REFERENCES

G. Rivière, *Le Maître Paul Cézanne* (1923), p. 196.
W. George, "The Twilight of a God," *Apollo*, 14 (1931),
    p. 77.
L. Venturi, *Cézanne: son art, son oeuvre* (1936), I, no. 79;
    II, pl. 21.
M. Raynal, *Cézanne* (1936), p. 146, pl. 58.
F. Novotny, *Paul Cézanne* (1937), pl. 2.
B. Dorival, *Cézanne* (1948), p. 142, pl. 27.
D. W. Steadman, "The Norton Simon Exhibition at
    Princeton," *Art Journal* (Fall 1972), pp. 34-40, repr. p. 38,
    Fig. 11.

EXHIBITIONS

London, Wildenstein & Co., Inc., "Hommage à Paul
    Cézanne," 1939, no. 3.
New York, Wildenstein & Co., Inc., "Cézanne," 1959, no. 4.
Philadelphia, Philadelphia Museum of Art, "The Francis
    Vogel Spitzer Collections," 1967.
Philadelphia, Philadelphia Museum of Art, "Recent
    Acquisitions by the Norton Simon, Inc. Museum of Art,"
    1969, no. 2.
Princeton, New Jersey, The Art Museum, Princeton
    University, "Selections from the Norton Simon, Inc.
    Museum of Art," 2 December 1972-June 1974, no. 32, repr.

COLLECTIONS

Auguste Pellerin;
J.-V. Pellerin;
Frances Vogel Spitzer;
Jane Wade, Ltd.;
Norton Simon Inc Foundation, Los Angeles (1968).

REMARKS

Cézanne made ten pictures using Dominique Aubert, his mother's brother, as the sole protagonist. In several of these Uncle Dominique posed as a monk, a lawyer, or a man coiffed in a turban. Although the remaining portraits abandoned the fantasy of disguise, their moods are similarly defiant, visionary and fiercely romantic. The Simon portrait is typical of the group in its concentration on the bust of the figure, its vigorous use of the palette knife and its bold modeling of rich black and brown tones relieved by accents of brighter color. Dominique's broad, thick features appealed to Cézanne. They permitted the projection of his own passionate feelings into the image of the sitter. Cézanne's interpretation of Dominique, as well as his treatment, resembles a sculptor's creation of rich plastic effect through cumulative planes of clay. Slabs of raw color, such as the swirl of red below the right eye, evoke an embroiled relief of pigment far removed from the texture of skin; but the vigor of Cézanne's knife is at the same time constrained by a prominent, black outline which is nearly incised around the head. This contrast of turbulent freedom and resolute control imbues the solidity and monumentality of Dominique's pose and distant gaze with a vivid sense of conflict and pathos.

K.H.

Vincent van Gogh

Born 1853 at Groot Zundert in the Netherlands; died 1890.

Biographical sketch in Volume I.

45. STILL LIFE (ca. 1884-1885)
Oil on canvas, 15-3/4 x 22 in. (40 x 55.9 cm.)

REFERENCES
J. DE LA FAILLE, *L'oeuvre de Vincent van Gogh, Catalogue Raisonné* (1928), no. 57.
J. DE LA FAILLE, *Vincent van Gogh* (1939), no. 62.
J. DE LA FAILLE, *The Works of Vincent van Gogh* (1970), p. 62.
Lettres à son Frère, Vol. II, no. 387.

COLLECTIONS
Dr. H. P. Bremmer, The Hague;
Arnold Hofland, London;
E. J. Van Wisselingh and Co., Amsterdam;
The Norton Simon Foundation, Los Angeles (1972).

REMARKS
This still life is one of a series that Van Gogh painted during his stay at Nuenen where he was teaching several local artisans the rudiments of his craft while struggling to find a style that met his expressive needs. The same crude, utilitarian objects recur throughout the series and are rendered in a similar primitive fashion. The background is painted in a cursory manner with a wide, coarse brush. The area in the upper left was quickly covered with a network of knitted horizontal and vertical strokes while the upper right was hardly touched. The forms of the household implements were treated with the same casualness. The contour of the wine bottle dissolves into the backdrop, flattening the picture and calling our attention to the material qualities of the surface of the canvas. The spontaneous appearance of this work conforms to the artist's frequently stated belief that good painting is done with *brio*. The inclination to rapidly set down his response to a motif is akin to that of the Impressionists, but his colors here are much different from their spectral hues. His palette was set with the dark, rich earth colors of the Dutch masters he revered. This heavy color scheme is also expressive of his love for the soil and those who till it. It may also reflect to some extent the deep melancholy that beset him the bleak winter this was painted. We might also say that this picture is, in a way, a visual metaphor for the artist's social beliefs. During this period he was under the influence of the work of Michelet and Zola and had come to believe that the vital force of society resided in the laboring class. These crude, misshapen objects have been in intimate daily contact with the rough-hewn peasants whom Van Gogh consecrated at their frugal repasts. This simple work, in contrast to the great tradition of still-life painting, might be termed a "proletarian" still life.
M.P.D.

46. PORTRAIT OF THE ARTIST'S MOTHER (1888)
Oil on canvas, 15-1/2 x 12-1/4 in. (39.5 x 31 cm.)

REFERENCES
G. COQUIOT, *Vincent van Gogh* (1923), p. 313.

J. DE LA FAILLE, *L'oeuvre de Vincent van Gogh* (1928), Vol. I, no. 477.

J. DE LA FAILLE, *Vincent van Gogh* (1939), no. H502.

F. ELGAR, *Van Gogh* (1958), no. 146.

V. VAN GOGH, *Complete Letters of Vincent van Gogh* (1958), III, nos. 546, 548.

M. TRALBAUT, *Van Gogh* (1960), p. 13.

R. WALLACE, *The World of van Gogh, 1853-1890* (1909), p. 8.

D. STEADMAN, "The Norton Simon Exhibition at Princeton," *Art Journal* (Fall 1972), pp. 34-40, p. 38 repr.

The Print Collector's Newsletter, IV, 4 (Sept.-Oct. 1973), p. 89, repr.

EXHIBITIONS
Berlin, Paul Cassirer, May-June 1914, no. 73.

Vienna, Secession, "Die führenden Meister der französischen Kunst im XIX Jahrhundert," 1925, no. 74.

Dresden, Internationale Kunstausstellung," 1926, no. 212.

New York, Wildenstein & Co., Inc., "Art and Life of Vincent van Gogh," 1943, no. 33.

Portland, Oregon, Portland Art Museum, "Recent Acquisitions by the Norton Simon, Inc. Museum of Art," November 1968-March 1969, no. 8.

Princeton, New Jersey, The Art Museum Princeton University, "Selections from the Norton Simon, Inc. Museum of Art," 2 December 1972-June 1974, no. 33, repr.

COLLECTIONS
Ambroise Vollard;

A. Rosenberg;

Carl Moll;

Paul Rosenberg & Co.;

Theodore Pitcairn (sale, Christie's, London, 28 June 1968, no. 122);

Norton Simon Inc Foundation, Los Angeles (1968).

REMARKS
This portrait was based on a black and white photograph which the artist found disturbingly colorless. According to a letter written to his brother Theo, Van Gogh had originally intended to paint the face ashen gray and the dress carmine (*Letters*, vol. III, no. 548). In all likelihood, the colors green and brown were selected in order to infuse the image with life by likening it to vegetation. This is seen in the rendering of both dress and hat. A sharp vertical brushstroke is employed in the brown dress which calls to mind the solidity of a tree trunk. In addition, the hat is composed of lively and variegated shapes which suggest growth. Its leafy quality and placement on the head resemble a crown of foliage. The portrayal of his mother in this guise is consistent with his attitude concerning portraiture. He frequently compared his sitters to natural objects referring to one of his portraits as "a star in the midst of an azure sky." Van Gogh creates a perfect harmony between man and nature with the implicit notion that they are made of the same substance. This painting suggests a deep psychological penetration. The eyes are framed with darker pigment than the rest of the face which accentuates their power by casting them into relief. The use of thick but energized brushwork imbues them with tension and sadness. Moreover, the gaze is unfocused, almost transfixed, and gives the face an air of gentle piety. Her sensitive eyes and softly rounded cheeks display the tender affections Van Gogh wished to express. The somewhat ambivalent relationship that existed between the artist and his mother is here translated into the most positive of terms.
M.S.

Georges Seurat

Born 1859 in Paris; died 1891.

Son of a bailiff and a devoted mother. As a highly disciplined student, he entered the École des Beaux-Arts in 1878 and gradually worked his way through the influence of Ingres, the Barbizon school and Impressionism. By 1881 he had read the color theories of Chevreul, Delacroix, Helmholtz, Rood and Charles Henry, and began to invent the Neo-Impressionist style he created out of a desire to eliminate the "superficial" feeling of transitory time. The formal structure of this composition was based on the Golden Section. The early development of this style began with his brilliant drawings and continued through such monumental masterpieces as *Sunday Afternoon on the Island of La Grande Jatte* of 1886 (Art Institute, Chicago). He was a solitary, secretive man whose highly conceptualized aesthetic theories helped him to develop paintings of extraordinary majesty. Continuing in the "rationalist" tradition of Piero della Francesca and Poussin, his influence was enormous.

47. THE STONEBREAKERS, LE RAINCY
(ca.1882)
Oil on canvas, 14-1/4 x 17-3/4 in. (33 x 45.5 cm.)

REFERENCES
J. DE LAPRADE, *Georges Seurat* (1945), pl. 3.
J. DE LAPRADE, *Seurat* (1951), pl. 10.
H. DORRA and J. REWALD, *Seurat: l'oeuvre peint, biographie et catalogue critique* (1959), no. 21.
C. M. DE HAUKE, *Seurat et son oeuvre* (1961), I, no. 38.
D. W. STEADMAN, "The Norton Simon Exhibition at Princeton," *Art Journal* (Fall 1972), pp. 34-40, repr. p. 37, Fig. 10.
D. W. STEADMAN, "The Landscape in Art," *University: A Princeton Quarterly* (Summer 1973), repr. p. 10.

EXHIBITIONS
Paris, Galerie Bernheim-Jeune, "Exposition Georges Seurat," 1908, no. 34.
Paris, Musée Jacquemart-André, "Seurat," 1957, no. 21.
Philadelphia, Philadelphia Museum of Art, "Recent Acquisitions by the Norton Simon, Inc. Museum of Art," no. 13.
Princeton, New Jersey, The Art Museum, Princeton University, "Selections from the Norton Simon, Inc. Museum of Art," 2 December 1972-June 1974, no. 31, repr.

COLLECTIONS
Jacques and Pierre Puybonnieux;
Léon Appert;
Léopold Appert;
Mme. Vve. Léopold Appert;
Private Collection, Paris;
Stephen Hahn Gallery;
The Norton Simon Inc Foundation, Los Angeles (1968).

REMARKS
Stonebreakers is one of seven works by Seurat dealing with the activities of peasant stonebreakers observed by the artist near his father's country estate at Le Raincy. The three figures, two of which are unexpectedly women, are virtually frozen at the midpoint of their hammers' arcs. In so minimizing the physical exertion of their labor, Seurat undercuts the social thrust evident in Courbet's treatment of the same subject. He transforms the bent figures into symbols of this impoverished class of nineteenth-century workers. Seurat's purpose was not simply to illustrate the unwieldy tools and the dreary passing from generation to generation of menial labor, but to explore the means of his own craft. Broken, criss-crossing strokes, varying from thin slashes to patches of broad pigment, indicate the young artist's interest in isolating the juxtaposing pure colors. While small in actual size, the painting suggests monumental scale through the isolation of simplified figures posed in frontal and profile views parallel to the picture surface. Seurat creates a sense of order and a mood of calm solemnity. As an experiment in rendering the effects of light in nature through divided color and brush stroke, *Stonebreakers* paralleled the aims of the Impressionists. But more importantly, the painting helped transform the Impressionist preoccupation with intuitive technique and the transitory character of nature. Seurat subordinated the experimental aspect of the work to a clearly ordered composition and a conception of the figure stressing abstraction. For this reason, *Stonebreakers, Le Raincy* was a milestone in Seurat's early career—a formation of the concerns which developed in complexity and sophistication during his subsequent monumental paintings.
K.H.

Paul Signac

Born 1868 in Paris; died 1935.

His well-to-do parents almost had persuaded him to become an architect when he saw the Monet exhibition of 1880 and decided to become a painter. He mastered the Impressionist technique under the inspiration of Monet and Guillaumin, and still had time to be mayor of Montmartre and secretary of *Le Chat noir*. In 1884 he co-founded the *Salon des Indépendants* and regularly organized its famous exhibitions. There he began his close friendship with Seurat, whom he showed how to replace brown tones with small colored strokes of Impressionism in the colors of the spectrum. Seurat and Cross, in turn, persuaded Signac to participate in the development of their technique. He shared the enthusiasm of his conversion with Pissarro, Van Gogh and the avant-garde in Brussels. When Seurat died in 1891, Signac assumed leadership of the Neo-Impressionist or Pointillist movement. He wrote the influential *From Delacroix to Neo-Impressionism* in 1899, which was quite meaningful to Matisse, Derain and the "Fauve" generation. From 1908 until his death, he continued to encourage young artists through his position as president of the Société des Artistes Indépendants.

48. SEINE AT LES ANDELYS 1886

Oil on canvas, 18 x 25-1/2 in. (46 x 65 cm.)
Dedicated, signed and dated, lower right:
"A mon ami Albert, P. Signac '86"

EXHIBITIONS

Portland, Portland Art Museum, "Recent Acquisitions by the Norton Simon, Inc. Museum of Art," November 1968-March 1969, no. 19.
Princeton, New Jersey, The Art Museum, Princeton University, "Selections from the Norton Simon, Inc. Museum of Art," 2 December 1972-June 1974, no. 35, repr.

COLLECTIONS

Private Collection (sale, Sotheby's, London, 23 October 1963, no. 54);
J. Horner;
Stephen Hahn Gallery;
Norton Simon Inc Foundation, Los Angeles (1968).

REMARKS

Although this painting is small, the conception of the landscape has a grandeur which is sustained by the broad, sweeping curve of the bank of the Seine, as well as by the mass and solidity of the hills behind the town. The tiny figure pushing a wheelbarrow up the ramp from the moored barge is the only sign of human activity. This figure provides the viewer with a visual point of reference where the foreground becomes the middleground. The church steeple and the tower to the left of the village serve the same function as the man: they anchor the middleground of the painting securely in front of the mountain in the background. These are the only strong verticals in a predominantly horizontal scheme. The horizontality is emphasized by the broad and discrete strokes of pure color which describe the surface of the river, the roofs of the houses and the striations in the hills behind. If we read the inscription correctly, the data of this work is a significant one in the history of the Impressionist movement. It marks a turn from the intuitive recording of optical sensations to a more scientific, calculated transcription of nature begun by Signac's friend Seurat. Both artists were included in the last Impressionist exhibition held that year. While the loose treatment of the water here shows the influence of Monet, the more methodical construction of the riverbank seems to owe something to the early work of Seurat.
R.L.

Henri Raymond de Toulouse-Lautrec

Born 1864 in Albi; died 1901.

Biographical sketch in Volume I.

49· RED-HAIRED WOMAN IN A GARDEN (1889)

Oil on cardboard, 28 x 23 in. (71 x 58.4 cm.)
Signed, upper right: "Lautrec"

REFERENCES

M. JOYANT, *Henri de Toulouse-Lautrec peintre* (1926), p. 267;
repr. p. 75.
E. SCHAUB-KOCH, *Psychanalyse d'un peintre moderne* (1935),
pp. 178, 190.
J. LASSAIGNE, *Toulouse-Lautrec* (trans. by M. Chamot) (1939),
p. 165, repr. p. 52.
The Connoisseur (American edition) (September 1959), repr.
p. 65.
J. ADHÉMAR and others, *Toulouse-Lautrec* (1962), p. 225.
G. CAPRONI and G. M. SUGANA, *L'opera completa di Toulouse-
Lautrec* (1969), p. 102, no. 233, repr. p. 102.
M. G. DORTU, *Toulouse-Lautrec et son oeuvre* (1971), II, p. 168,
no. 342, repr. p. 169.

EXHIBITIONS

Paris, Galerie Manzi-Joyant, "Exposition rétrospective de
Toulouse-Lautrec," 1914, no. 27.
Toronto, Art Gallery of Ontario, 1927.
Chicago, Art Institute of Chicago, "Loan Exhibition of
Paintings, Drawings, Prints, and Posters," 23 December
1930-18 January 1931, no. 10.
New York, Museum of Modern Art, "Toulouse-Lautrec and
Redon," 1 February-2 March 1931, no. 10, repr.
Buffalo, Albright Art Gallery, "19th-Century French Art,"
1-30 November, 1932, no. 60.
New York, Wildenstein & Co., Inc., "Toulouse-Lautrec,"
23 October-23 November 1946, no. 5, repr.
New York, Wildenstein & Co., Inc., "Toulouse-Lautrec,"
7 February-14 March 1964, no. 19, repr.
Washington, D.C., The National Gallery of Art, "French
Paintings from the Collection of Mr. and Mrs. Paul Mellon
and Mrs. Mellon Bruce," 17 March-1 May 1966, no. 151,
repr.

COLLECTIONS

Nardus Collection;
Pierre Decourcelle, Paris (sale, Hôtel Drouot, Paris, 16 June
1926, no. 74, repr.);
Paul Rosenberg & Co., Paris and New York;
Albright Art Gallery, Buffalo (1926-43);
Wildenstein & Co., Inc., New York;
Thelma Chrysler Foy, New York (sale, Parke-Bernet, New
York, 13 May 1959, no. 12; repr. in color p. 29);
Gordon Guiberson, Bel Air;
Mr. and Mrs. Paul Mellon, Virginia;
Wildenstein & Co., Inc., New York;
The Norton Simon Foundation, Los Angeles (1973).

REMARKS

This work suggests how firmly Toulouse-Lautrec's painting is rooted in the Impressionist style of the 1870s and 1880s. The motif of a woman in a garden or conservatory was a common one; numerous examples are to be found among the work of such artists as Renoir and Monet. The technique, too, draws upon Impressionist devices. The brushwork is loose, sketchy, and spontaneous. A pastel-like quality is evoked, particularly in the delicate crosshatching of the face; strokes are used as if by a draughtsman rather than a painter. Note the profile outline of the head. Color functions descriptively, not structurally. The artist treats the shadows not as black, but as colored phenomena. Daylight falls from the right; it is depicted by bold, horizontal brushstrokes across the model's shoulders and back, while those shadows under her breasts and arms are of the same purple hue as her dress. The picture is painted on brown cardboard advantageously utilized to suggest skin and earth tones. It is visible under the transparent dress, as well as under the foliage of the garden. Toulouse-Lautrec had a predilection for red-haired women. The identity of the model is unknown, although he painted her again at least once. The garden belonged to M. Forest, a photographer friend of the artist's, sometimes known as Père Forest. The model's pose is unusual: a three-quarter view from behind and a profile head. Her gaze is directed downward, pensive but not melancholic. There is a profound detachment and a treatment of the sitter as an object, both qualities reminiscent of Degas, whom Toulouse-Lautrec revered. Yet the anonymity of the poses is offset by the intensity of the color.
R.A.

113

Odilon Redon

Born 1840 in Bordeaux; died 1916.

Redon began to develop his dream-like images during his lonely childhood on his uncle's isolated estate near Bordeaux. There he drew the crumbling walls, the wild grass and the clouds. Helping him articulate the vague feelings he had about what is "inside" things were two important teachers—Clavaud, a naturalist who introduced him to "avant-garde" poetry and the exterior structure of living things; and Bresdin, an enigmatic etcher, filled with extraordinary visions and the capacity to draw them out. In the 1870s, Redon moved to Paris. There, after a brief stay in Gérôme's studio, he continued to cultivate the infinitely rich garden of his unconscious mind under the inspiration of Goya, Poe, Flaubert and Baudelaire, Mallarmé and Valéry. Until about 1890, he used only black and white media. His move to color corresponded with a growing recognition of the value of his revolutionary "message": interior realities are just as important as exterior realities. This fact and his work exerted considerable influence on Gauguin, the Nabis and many other Symbolists, as well as Matisse and the Surrealists. His historical position as an important bridge between centuries is emphasized by the fact that he was represented by more works than any other artist in the New York Armory Show of 1913.

REMARKS

Redon's painting is a copy of a work by Cézanne which was published in Volume I of this catalogue, Plate 43. Redon has preserved the elements of Cézanne's painting, but the effect of the image is much more natural than the vigorous ambiguity in the work by Cézanne. This is obvious in the four orchid-colored flowers that decorate the wallpaper behind the vase. In Cézanne's painting, they seem to hover in an indeterminate space, while in the copy by Redon they are more a part of the wall. Redon presents a more convincing illusion of three-dimensional space by changing the width of the bands of green and red that mark the boundary between the table and the background. By making the colors purer and widening the band of green, he made the table more concrete. This in turn allowed him to paint the vase of flowers as a solid object, taking up real space. While Cézanne's approach to his motif was experimental and conceptual, Redon deintellectualized the image and made it more obviously real.
R.L.

50. VASE OF FLOWERS (Copy after Cézanne)
(1896)
Oil on canvas, 18-1/4 x 21-3/4 in.
(46.4 x 55.2 cm.)

REFERENCES
R. BACOU, *Odilon Redon* (1956), I, p. 176.
K. BERGER, *Odilon Redon* (1964), no. 260.

EXHIBITIONS
Paris, Petit Palais, "Redon," 1934.
Paris, Galerie Charpentier, "Natures Mortes Françaises," 1951.
The Hague, Gemeente Museum, "Redon," 3 May-23 June 1957, no. 178.
Finistere, Marie de Pont-Aven, "Gauguin et ses amis," 1961, no. 146.

COLLECTIONS
A. Leblond, Paris;
E. J. van Wisselingh & Co., Amsterdam;
Neison Harris, Chicago;
Norton Simon Inc Foundation, Los Angeles (1973)
Gift of Nieson Harris.

115

Edouard Vuillard

Born 1868 in Cuiseaux, near Lyon; died 1940.

Son of an army officer and a dressmaker. In 1886 he entered the class of Gérôme at the *École des Beaux-Arts*, where his childhood friends, Maurice Denis and Xavier Roussel, introduced him to Bonnard, Ranson, Vallotton and Sérusier. Together they formed a group called the "Nabis" (the Hebrew word for prophets or *illuminati*) and exhibited together during the 1890s. Like most members of the "Nabis," Vuillard was influenced by the Symbolist style of the late Degas and Monet, Gauguin, Bernard and Redon, as well as Japanese prints. He worked with equal enthusiasm in many media: lithographs for Vollard, decorative panels for the editor of *Revue Blanche*, a stained-glass window for Tiffany, and murals for the Palace of the League of Nations in Geneva. Most of his subjects are domestic interiors. In 1938 he was elected to the Institute de France and was given a major retrospective at the Musée des Arts Décoratifs. The career of this shy, lyric poet quietly testifies to his simple assumption that art and life are not two entirely separate things.

51. FIRST FRUITS 1899

Oil on canvas, 96 x 170 in. (243.8 x 431.8 cm.)
Signed and dated, lower right: "E Vuillard 1899"

REFERENCES
A. SEGARD, *Peintres d'aujourd'hui: les décorateurs* (1914), II, pp. 253, 262-266, 321.
C. ROGER-MARX, *Vuillard et son temps* (1945), pp. 138-139.
A. CHASTEL, *Vuillard* (1946), pp. 53, 115.
C. ROGER-MARX, *Vuillard* (1948), p. 43, Fig. 25.
R. BACOU, "Décors d'appartements au temps des Nabis," *Art de France*, IV (1964), p. 196.
Antiques (November 1964), p. 622, repr.
J. DUGDALE, "Vuillard the Decorator—I. First Phase: the 1890's," *Apollo* (February 1965), p. 99.

EXHIBITIONS
Paris, Musée des Arts Décoratifs, "Exposition E. Vuillard," May-July 1938, no. 69.
Portland, Portland Art Museum, "Paintings from the Collection of Walter P. Chrysler, Jr." 1956, no. 87. (Exhibition also at Seattle Art Museum; California Palace of the Legion of Honor, San Francisco; Los Angeles County Museum; Minneapolis Institute of Art; City Art Museum of St. Louis; William Rockhill Nelson Gallery of Art, Kansas City; Detroit Institute of Arts; Museum of Fine Arts, Boston.)
New York, Wildenstein & Co., Inc., "Vuillard," 16 October-21 November 1964, no. 22, repr. in color.

COLLECTIONS
Adam Natanson, Paris;
Thadée Natanson, Paris (sale, Hôtel Drouot, Paris, 13 June 1908, no. 63);
Alexandre Natanson, Paris (sale, Hôtel Drouot, Paris, 16 May 1929, no. 126, repr.);
Léon Blum, Paris;
Walter P. Chrysler, Jr., New York;
Private Collection, Switzerland;
Wildenstein & Co., Inc., New York;
The Norton Simon Foundation, Los Angeles (1973).

REMARKS
The intimacy which Vuillard brought to his interiors is retained in this interpretation of peasant life in the country. His view of the relationship of man to nature is unlike that of many of his contemporaries. Nature is not hemmed in by mankind. Man and his structures, cushioned in the landscape, create an integrated whole. The quiet stasis of compact, unindividualized figures remains unobtrusive within the landscape. In their simplified fullness they echo the voluminous lushness of the vegetation which surrounds them. The expression of peace and well-being of man in nature is enhanced by the soft quality of line. The wide arcs of foliage and gently rolling hills echo one another in rhythmic curves. The brightness of flowers larger than life, scattered through the chastened tans and greens of the foreground, adds a note of gaiety to this idyllic work scene. Size, clarity, and detail of the figures and foliage are highly inconsistent with their actual location in space. In accordance with the Nabis' desire to restore painting to its primary function (the adornment of surfaces), complicated illusionistic devices have been rejected in favor of flat, decorative schemes. To further strengthen this tapestry-like scheme, Vuillard has painted a framing border which includes flowers, foliage, and earth. The quotidian subject of the painting, its accessibility to all levels of society, and its large size are attempts to break down the barriers between art and life. This picture is one of a pair painted for the study of Adam Natanson, a co-founder of the *Revue Blanche*. The panels, each a length of over fourteen feet, were among the largest pieces ever painted by Vuillard. The companion piece to this work is also a landscape of the Île-de-France.
L.P.

Pierre Bonnard

Born 1867 in Fontenay-aux-Roses; died 1947.

Biographical sketch in Volume I.

52. PORTRAIT OF LEILA CLAUDE ANET
(1930)
Oil on canvas, 49 x 32-5/8 in. (124.5 x 82.9 cm.)
Signed, lower right: "Bonnard"

REFERENCES
J. & H. DAUBERVILLE, *Bonnard, Catalogue raisonné de l'oeuvre peint* (4 vols., 1965-1974), III (1920-1939), no. 1458, repr. p. 362.
J. GALLEGO, "Crónica de Paris," *Goya* (November-December 1960), pp. 216-217, repr. p. 217.

EXHIBITIONS
Paris, Galerie Charpentier, "Cent tableaux de collections privées," April-June 1960, no. 4.
Paris, Galerie Braun, "Portraits de Pierre Bonnard," June 1933.

COLLECTIONS
Mrs. Jean Mabilleau (Leila Claude Anet), Paris;
Robert Ellis Simon (1967);
The Norton Simon Foundation, Los Angeles (1969).

REMARKS
Despite the stiff pose of the sitter and the function of this painting, which makes it a modern cousin to a type of eighteenth-century society portrait, it shows an extraordinary degree of sympathetic affection for the model. Bonnard approaches the figure and setting in terms of a personal love for pattern and color. The magic of this portrait derives from contrasts in tone and texture and from the interplay of three-dimensional form and flat surface. The effect is one of intriguing ambiguity which serves to evoke the elusive temperament of the sitter. The warm glow of the highly textured face is speckled with green and gray, the auburn hair lightly traced with white. In contrast, both sweater and skirt are depicted by areas of bare canvas rubbed in several places with a film of white, quickly brushed with lines of blue. The skirt has been playfully composed of three discordant triangles. Scruples of anatomical precision are disregarded in the rendering of the crossed legs as though both were contained on the left side of the body. This painting was commissioned by Claude Anet, Leila's father, a writer and lifelong friend of Bonnard. The picture replaces a smaller portrait rejected by both client and artist. After only three sittings, Bonnard put in the finishing touches in December 1930 and brought it to the ailing Claude Anet who chose the frame. When Monsieur Anet died a month later, the artist gave the portrait to Leila's mother as a token of friendship.
T.C.

General Bibliography

The Selected Bibliography in Volume I was prepared for those who are starting to become interested in French Art and would like to read general surveys of eras and centuries. This longer bibliography was designed for those who would like to study individual French artists in more detail. The artists from Volume I and Volume II have been represented in this general bibliography.

BAZILLE
François Daulte. "Bazille; son oeuvre s'achève en 1870," *Connaissance des Arts* (December 1970)

BOILLY
Henry Harrisse. *Louis Léopold Boilly: peintre, dessinateur, et lithographie; sa vie et son oeuvre (1761-1845)*. Paris: Société de Propagation des Livres d'Art (1898)

BONNARD
Jean and Henry Dauberville. *Bonnard: catalogue raisonné de l'oeuvre peint*. Paris: Bernheim (4 vols. 1965-1974)

John Rewald. *Pierre Bonnard*. New York: Museum of Modern Art (1948)

BOUCHER
André Michel. *François Boucher*. Paris (n.d.)

Pierre de Nolhac. *François Boucher*. Paris: Goupil (1907)

BOUDIN
Gustave Cahen. *Eugène Boudin, sa vie et son oeuvre*. Paris: Floury (1900)

G. Jean-Aubry and Robert Schmit. *Eugène Boudin*. Greenwich: New York Graphic Society (1968)

CASSATT
Adelyn Breeskin. *Mary Cassatt: a Catalogue Raisonné of the Oils, Pastels, Watercolors, and Drawings*. Washington, D.C.: Smithsonian Institution (1970)

CEZANNE
Roger Fry. *Cézanne, a Study of his Development*. New York: Macmillan (1927)

Lionello Venturi. *Cézanne, son art-son oeuvre*. Paris: Paul Rosenberg (2 vols. 1936)

Meyer Schapiro. *Paul Cézanne*. New York: Abrams (1952)

Fritz Novotny. *Paul Cézanne*. New York: Phaidon (1961)

John Rewald. *Paul Cézanne, A Biography*. New York: Schocken (1967)

Sandra Orienti and Alfonso Gatto. *L'Opera completa di Cézanne*. Milan: Rizzoli (1970)

CHARDIN
Armand P. M. Dayot, *J.-B. Siméon Chardin* (avec un catalogue complet de l'oeuvre du maître par Jean Guiffrey). Paris: Piazza (1907)

Georges Wildenstein. *Chardin*. Paris: Les Beaux-Arts (1921)

Daniel Wildenstein. *Chardin*. Greenwich: New York Graphic Society (1969)

DEVERIA
Jean Guiffrey. "Achille et Eugène Devéria: leur vie et leur oeuvre," *L'Art*, XXXII (1883)

CLAUDE
Claude Lorrain. *Liber Veritatis*. (A collection of prints, after the original designs of Claude de Lorrain, in the collection of His Grace, the Duke of Devonshire. Now in the British Museum.) London: Boydell (3 vols. 1777-1819)

Marcel Roethlisberger. *Claude Lorrain; the paintings*. New Haven: Yale University Press (2 vols. 1961)

COROT
Alfred Robaut and Etienne Moreau-Nélaton. *L'oeuvre de Corot*. Paris: Floury (5 vols. 1905) (reprint 1965-1966)

Jean Leymarie. *Corot*. Translated by S. Gilbert. Cleveland: World (Skira) (1966)

COURBET
Charles Léger. *Courbet et son temps*. Paris: Editions Universelles (1948)

Gerstle Mack. *Gustave Courbet*. New York: Knopf (1951)

DAUBIGNY
Etienne Moreau-Nélaton. *Daubigny, raconté par lui-même*. Paris: Laurens (1925)

Madeleine Fidell-Beaufort and Janine Bailly-Herzberg. *Daubigny (la vie et l'oeuvre)*. Paris: Editions Geoffroy-Dechaume (1975)

DAUMIER
Karl E. Maison. *Honoré Daumier; catalogue raisonné of the paintings, watercolours, and drawings*. Greenwich: New York Graphic Society (2 vols. 1967)

Oliver Larkin. *Daumier: Man of His Time*. Boston: Beacon (1968)

DEGAS

Paul Lafond. *Degas*. Paris: Floury (2 vols. 1918-1919)

Paul A. Lemoisne. *Degas et son oeuvre*. Paris: Brame (4 vols. 1947)

John Rewald. *Degas: Sculpture, The Complete Works*. New York: Abrams (1956)

DELACROIX

Alfred Robaut. *L'oeuvre complet de Eugène Delacroix, peintures, dessins, gravures, lithographies*. Paris: Charavay (1885)

Raymond Escholier. *Delacroix, peintre, graveur, écrivain*. Paris: Floury (3 vols. 1926-1929)

Charles Baudelaire. *Eugène Delacroix, his life and work*, Translated by J. M. Bernstein. New York: Lear (1947)

Rene Huyghe. *Delacroix*. New York: Abrams (1963)

DEVERIA

Jean Guiffrey. "Achille et Eugène Devéria: leur vie et leur oeuvre," *L'Art*, XXXII (1883)

FANTIN-LATOUR

Victoria D. Fantin-Latour. *Catalogue de l'oeuvre complet de Fantin-Latour*. Paris: Floury (1911 & 1969)

FRAGONARD

Roger Portalis. *Honoré Fragonard, sa vie et son oeuvre*. Paris: Rothschild (2 vols. 1889)

Pierre de Nolhac. *Fragonard*. Paris: Goupil (1918)

Georges Wildenstein. *Paintings of Fragonard*. Translated by C. W. Chilton and A. L. Kitson. New York: Phaidon (1960)

Jacques Thuillier. *Fragonard*. Geneva: Skira (1967)

GAUGUIN

Robert Goldwater. *Gauguin*. New York: Abrams (1957)

Georges Wildenstein. *Gauguin*. Paris: Beaux-Arts (1964)

Bengt Danielsson. *Gauguin in the South Seas*. New York: Doubleday (1965)

GUIGOU

Mon Cher Guigou. Paris: Galérie Daber (1970)

GUILLAUMIN

G. Serret and D. Fabian. *Armand Guillaumin, 1841-1927, catalogue raisonné de l'oeuvre peint*. Paris: Mayer (1971)

Christopher Gray. *Guillaumin*. Chester: Pequot Press (1972)

INGRES

Walter Pach. *Ingres*. New York: Harper (1939)

Georges Wildenstein. *Ingres*. London: Phaidon (1954)

E. Radius. *L'Opera completa di Ingres*. Milan: Rizzoli (1968)

JONGKIND

Etienne Moreau-Nélaton. *Jongkind raconté par lui-même*. Paris: Laurens (1918)

Claude Roger-Marx. *Jongkind*. Paris: Crès (1932)

LARGILLIERE

George Pascal. *Largillière*. Paris: Beaux-Arts (1928)

LA TOUR

Albert Besnard and Georges Wildenstein. *La Tour; la vie et l'oeuvre de l'artiste*. Paris: Beaux-Arts (1928)

Adrian Bury. *Maurice-Quentin de La Tour: the Greatest Pastel Portraitist*. London: Charles Skilton Ltd. (1971)

MAILLOL

Waldemar George. *Maillol*. Greenwich: New York Graphic Society (1965)

MANET

Paul Jamot and Georges Wildenstein. *Manet*. Paris: Beaux-Arts (1932)

George Hamilton. *Manet and his critics*. New Haven: Yale (1954)

Sandre Orienti and Phoebe Pool. *The Complete Paintings of Manet*. New York: Abrams (1967)

MOILLON

Jacques Wilhelm. "Louise Moillon," *L'Oeil* (September 1956)

MONET

Gustave Geffroy. *Claude Monet, sa vie, son oeuvre*. Paris: Crès (2 vols. 1924)

Camille Mauclair. *Claude Monet*. Translated by J. L. May. New York: Dodd (1924)

William Seitz. *Claude Monet*. New York: Abrams (1960)

PATER

Florence Ingersoll-Smouse. *Pater: biographie et catalogue critique, l'oeuvre complet de l'artiste*. Paris: Beaux-Arts (1928)

PISSARRO

Ludovic R. Pissarro. *Camille Pissaro, son art, son oeuvre*. Paris: Paul Rosenberg (1939)

POUSSIN

Anthony Blunt. *The Paintings of Nicolas Poussin, a Critical Catalogue*. New York: Phaidon (1966)

Anthony Blunt. *Nicolas Poussin*. Princeton: Princeton University (2 vols. 1966)

PUVIS DE CHAVANNES

A. Alexandre. "Puvis de Chavannes et son oeuvre," *Le Figaro Illustre*, 17 (1899)

Camille Mauclair. *Puvis de Chavannes.* Paris: Plon (1928)

REDON

André Mellerio. *Odilon Redon, peintre, dessinateur et graveur.* Paris: Floury (1923)

Roseline Bacou. *Odilon Redon.* Geneva: Cailler (2 vols. 1956)

Klaus Berger. *Odilon Redon; fantasy and colour.* Translated by Michael Bullock. New York: McGraw (1965)

RENOIR

Ambroise Vollard. *Tableaux, pastels, et dessins de Pierre Auguste Renoir.* Paris: Vollard (2 vols. 1918)

Julius Meier-Graefe. *Renoir.* Leipzig: Klinhardt (1929)

François Daulte. *Auguste Renoir: catalogue raisonné de l'oeuvre peint.* Lausanne (1971)

RIGAUD

Joseph Roman. *Le livre de raison du peintre Hyacinthe Rigaud.* Paris: Laurens (1919)

ROBERT

Pierre de Nolhac. *Hubert Robert, 1733-1808.* Paris: Goupil (1910)

Tristan Leclère. *Hubert Robert et les paysagistes français de XVIIIe siècle.* Paris: Laurens (1913)

RODIN

Georges Grappe. *Le Musée Rodin.* Paris: Taupin (1947)

Albert Elsen. *Rodin.* New York: Museum of Modern Art (1963)

Judith Cladel. *Rodin, the man and his art.* New York: Viking (1967)

ROUSSEAU

Pierre Courthion. *Henri Rousseau, le douanier.* Geneva: Skira (1944)

Daniel C. Rich. *Henri Rousseau.* New York: Museum of Modern Art (1946)

SEURAT

Jacques de Laprade. *Georges Seurat.* Monaco: Taupin (1945)

John Rewald and Henry Dorra. *Georges Seurat.* New York: Wittenborn (1946)

Anthony Blunt. *Seurat.* New York: Phaidon (1965)

SIGNAC

George Besson. *Signac, dessins.* Paris: Braun (1950)

Françoise Cachin. *Paul Signac.* Greenwich: New York Graphic Society (1971)

SISLEY

François Daulte. *Alfred Sisley: catalogue raisonné de l'oeuvre peint.* Lausanne: Durand-Ruel (1959)

STOSKOPFF

Hans Haug. "Sebastien Stoskopff," *L'Oeil*, 76 (April 1961)

TOULOUSE-LAUTREC

Maurice Joyant. *Henri de Toulouse-Lautrec, 1864-1901.* Paris: Floury (2 vols. 1926-1927)

Jean Adhémar *et al. Toulouse-Lautrec.* Paris: Hachette (1962)

G. Caproni and G. M. Sugana. *L'Opera completa di Toulouse-Lautrec.* Milan: Rizzoli (1969)

VAN GOGH

J. Bernard de La Faille. *L'oeuvre de Vincent van Gogh; catalogue raisonné.* Paris: Van Oest (4 vols. 1928)

Meyer Schapiro. *Vincent Van Gogh.* New York: Abrams (1950)

VERNET

Charles Blanc. *Une famille d'artistes, les trois Vernet: Joseph, Carle, Horace.* Paris: Rénouard (1898)

Florence Ingersoll-Smouse. *Joseph Vernet, peintre de marine, 1714-1789.* Paris: Bignou (2 vols. 1926)

VESTIER

P. Dorbec. "Antoine Vestier," *La Revue de l'Art Ancien et Moderne*, XXXIX (1911)

VIGEE-LEBRUN

Pierre de Nolhac. *Madame Vigée-Lebrun, Peintre de la Reine Marie Antoinette.* Paris: Goupil (1908)

William H. Helm. *Vigée-Lebrun, Her Life, Works, and Friendships.* Boston: Small, Maynard & Co. (1915)

VUILLARD

Claude Roger-Marx. *Vuillard et son temps.* Paris: Editions Arts et Métiers Graphiques (1945)

John Russell. *Vuillard.* London: Thames & Hudson (1971)

WATTEAU

Hélène Adhémar. *Watteau, sa vie, son oeuvre.* Paris: Tisné (1950)

Ettore Camesasca. *The Complete Paintings of Watteau.* New York: Abrams (1968)

STAFF